Geometry

Sunshine State Standards Support Book

The Sunshine State Standards Support Book helps prepare students for the Grade 10 FCAT. The Support Book begins with a Florida Pacing Guide that helps integrate FCAT practice into the course on an ongoing basis. The Support Book also includes examples and practice for benchmarks assessed on the FCAT, FCAT diagnostic tests, practice with gridding answers to gridded response questions, plus a variety of other materials to help students develop the test-taking skills they need to succeed on the FCAT. For a complete overview of the Support Book contents, see pages vi–vii.

McDougal Littell

A HOUGHTON MIFFLIN COMPANY

Evanston, Illinois • Boston • Dallas

Florida Curriculum and Assessment Advisor
Barbara Nunn, Secondary Mathematics Specialist,
Broward County Schools, Fort Lauderdale, Florida.

ISBN: 0-618-41632-3

3456789–BHV–07 06 05 04

Contents

Using the Support Book	vi
Florida Pacing Guide	P1
Correlation to Florida Benchmarks	P15

FCAT Handbook

About the FCAT	H1
How to Prepare for the FCAT	H2
Solving Word Problems	H4
Gridded-Response Questions	H9
Gridding Sheet	H12
FCAT Mathematics Reference Sheet	H13

Support Book Sheets

Module 1

Integers	1
Patterns	2
Order of Operations	4
Representing Numbers	5
Circles, Graphs, and Angles	6
Solving Linear Equations	8
Distance and Midpoint Formulas	9
Use a Variety of Formulas	10
Solve Measurement Problems	12
Computing with Rational Numbers	14
FCAT Spiral Review 1	16

Module 2

Range and Measures of Central Tendency	17
Interpreting Graphs	19
Using Properties to Simplify Expressions	22
Solving and Using Linear Equations	23
Comparing and Ordering Numbers	24
Angle Pair Relationships	25
Operations with Exponents	26
FCAT Spiral Review 2	28

Module 3

Powers of 10 and Scientific Notation	29
Angle Pair Relationships and Perpendicular Lines	30
Parallel Lines and Transversals	31
Properties of Parallel Lines	32
Linear Relationships	33
Parallelism and Perpendicularity	35
Step Functions	36
FCAT Spiral Review 3	38

Module 4

Rewriting Formulas	39
Angles in Triangles	40
Congruent Triangles	41
Applying Congruent Triangles	42
Special Triangles	44
Triangles on Coordinate Grids	45
Perpendicular and Angle Bisectors	46
Equations, Expressions, and Inequalities	47
FCAT Spiral Review 4	49

Module 5

Solving Linear Inequalities	50
Triangle Inequalities	52
Finding an Unknown Angle	53
Properties of Parallelograms	55
Interpreting Venn Diagrams	56
Properties of Quadrilaterals	58
Solving for Area and Perimeter	60
Using Percents	62
FCAT Spiral Review 5	64

Module 6

Symmetry	65
Graphs of Parabolas	67
Transformations	69
Systems of Equations and Inequalities	70
FCAT Spiral Review 6	72

Module 7

Proportional Reasoning	73
Similar Triangles and Slope	75
Recognizing and Using Similar Triangles	76
Percent of Increase and Decrease	77
Dilations	78
Indirect Measurement	79
Sampling and Surveys	80
FCAT Spiral Review 7	82

Module 8

Square Roots	83
Using the Pythagorean Theorem	84
Converse of the Pythagorean Theorem	85
Function Tables	86
Angle Measures in Polygons	87
Perimeters and Areas of Similar Figures	88
Arc Lengths	89
Areas of Circles and Sectors	90

Introduction to Probability   91
Independent and Dependent Events   92
Scatter Plots   93
FCAT Spiral Review 8   94

Module 9
Cross Sections of Solids   95
Surface Area   96
Volume   97
Similar Solids   98
FCAT Spiral Review 9   99

Florida Assessment Materials
Mid-Module 1 Quiz   101
Module 1 Test   102
Mid-Module 2 Quiz   104
Module 2 Test   105
Mid-Module 3 Quiz   107
Module 3 Test   108
Modules 1–3 Cumulative Test   110

Mid-Module 4 Quiz   114
Module 4 Test   115
Mid-Module 5 Quiz   117
Module 5 Test   118
Mid-Module 6 Quiz   120
Module 6 Test   121
Modules 1–6 Cumulative Test   123

Mid-Module 7 Quiz   127
Module 7 Test   128
Mid-Module 8 Quiz   130
Module 8 Test   131
Mid-Module 9 Quiz   133
Module 9 Test   134
Modules 1–9 Cumulative Test   136

Mid-Module 10 Quiz   140
Module 10 Test   141
Mid-Module 11 Quiz   143
Module 11 Test   144
Mid-Module 12 Quiz   146
Module 12 Test   147

FCAT Diagnostic Test 1   149
FCAT Diagnostic Test 2   156

FCAT Diagnostic Test 1 Answer Sheets   163
FCAT Diagnostic Test 2 Answer Sheets   168

Using the Support Book

Florida Pacing Guide The Florida Pacing Guide shows how to pace the material in the course into manageable *Modules* so that all of the benchmarks assessed on the FCAT are addressed by the time the test is administered. The Pacing Guide specifies which textbook lessons and Support Book sheets should be covered each day.

FCAT Handbook The FCAT Handbook provides information and tips to help students be successful on the test. It includes an overview of the FCAT, test-taking tips, strategies for solving word problems, instructions for completing gridded-response questions, and an FCAT Reference Sheet with formulas and conversions.

Gridding Sheet A reproducible sheet with twelve blank grids is provided for use in conjunction with the Module Tests and Cumulative Tests so that students can gain experience completing grids in a testing situation. These grids may also be used with many of the Support Book sheets at the Teacher's discretion. Spaces are provided to write in the appropriate exercise numbers.

FCAT Examples and Exercises These Support Book sheets include worked-out examples and practice exercises that address specific benchmarks and grade level expectations being assessed on the FCAT. They provide practice with both multiple-choice and open-response questions. The Teacher may also elect to have students grid answers to selected problems on a copy of the Gridding Sheet. These Support Book sheets can be used in a variety of ways: before a class lesson, as a class lesson, or following a lesson as part of a homework assignment. The Florida Pacing Guide suggests how these pages can be integrated into the course on a regular basis.

FCAT Spiral Review The FCAT Spiral Review pages are interspersed with the Support Book sheets to coincide with the module breaks in the Pacing Guide. They consist of exercises that practice benchmarks or grade level expectations covered in the preceding module and in previous modules.

Mid-Module Quizzes A brief one-page quiz is provided for every module to assess progress on the first half of the module. The quizzes consist of multiple-choice and gridded-response questions. Students record their answers directly on the quiz sheet.

Module Tests A two-page test is provided at the end of every module. The tests consist of multiple-choice, gridded-response, short-response, and extended-response questions. Students record answers to the gridded-response questions on the separate Gridding Sheet.

Cumulative Tests A four-page test is provided at the end of Modules 3, 6, and 9. The tests are cumulative to the beginning of the course. The tests consist of multiple-choice, gridded-response, short-response, and extended-response questions. Students record answers to the gridded-response questions on the separate Gridding Sheet.

FCAT Diagnostic Tests The FCAT Diagnostic Tests cover the key content of the entire course and all of the benchmarks assessed on the FCAT. There are two parallel forms of the test, 1 and 2. They can be used as a pre-course or post-course diagnostic test. Because the order of the test items matches the order of the course content, the pre-FCAT section of the course assessments (Exercises 1–44) can also be used as a practice test for the FCAT. The questions are in multiple-choice, gridded-response, short-response, and extended-response format. Separate **Answer Sheets** similar to those used for the FCAT are provided to record answers.

FLORIDA PACING GUIDE

The goal of the Florida Pacing Guide is two-fold: to cover all geometry topics required for the Grade 10 FCAT before the test is administered and to incorporate into the day-by-day course-work a review of all non-geometry topics required for the Grade 10 FCAT. To accomplish this, a number of adjustments have been made in the organization and pacing of the course. Certain textbook lessons or parts of lessons are postponed until after the FCAT or are treated in ways that save time. In addition, FCAT topics that are not in the textbook lessons are addressed with a variety of supplemental materials, either for use during class time or as part of the homework. This review is spiralled throughout the course with connections made, when possible, to the ongoing geometry lessons. The resulting Florida Pacing Guide organizes the course into Modules 1–9 to be covered before the FCAT and Modules 10–12 to be covered after the FCAT.

Lesson Materials The "Lesson Materials" column of the chart shows the materials to be used for in-class instruction on each day or group of two days. These materials include textbook lessons (listed by lesson number), pages in the Skills Review Handbook (SRH) and appendices (App.) located at the back of the textbook, and pages from the Algebra Review sections (Alg. Rev.) located after the even numbered chapters. Lessons from an ancillary called the *Data Analysis Sourcebook* (DAS) and pages from this Support Book (SB) are also listed. A single day or group of two days may cover more than one element (e.g., a textbook lesson and a Support Book page).

Unless otherwise noted, the module quizzes and tests do not specifically assess the non-geometry content that is reviewed through supplemental materials, even if class time is spent on it. The cumulative tests and the FCAT Diagnostic Test, on the other hand, assess both geometry and non-geometry topics whether they are covered in class or just reviewed as homework.

Notes The suggestions in the "Notes" column include key concepts to stress, specific examples and/or exercises to omit, and additional resources to use. Based on importance for the Florida benchmarks and time constraints, advice is given about whether or not to include activities associated with lessons. Note that the Alg. Rev., SRH, and/or DAS may contain additional examples and exercises on number, algebra, and data topics even when this has not been noted.

Support Book Sheets If a lesson has one or more "correlated" Support Book sheets, the page numbers have been listed in the "Page(s) in Support Book (SB)" column. A sheet may address key content in that lesson, make some other connection to the lesson (e.g., review a skill applied in the lesson), or be placed with the lesson for the overall spiralling of review. In some cases, one support book sheet will correlate to the content of several lessons. If a sheet is to be used in class, it will be listed in the lesson materials column and its use discussed in the notes column. Otherwise, the sheet can be completed by students as homework at the indicated time.

Reorganization of Content Topics postponed until after the FCAT include most compass constructions, many triangle properties, circle relationships, and trigonometry. Care has been taken to maintain a sequence in which students are given all the theorems needed for later proofs.

FLORIDA PACING GUIDE

BEFORE THE FCAT

Module 1 (Chapter 1) Basics of Geometry

Day	Lesson Materials	Notes	Page(s) in Support Book (SB)	Benchmarks Covered in SB
1	1.1 & SB p. 1	Cover Goal 1. Also, spend some class time reviewing integer operations using SB. If students need additional work on integer operations, you may wish to use the examples and exs. involving integers from SRH p. 785.	p. 1	MA.A.1.4.3, MA.A.2.4.2, MA.A.3.4.1, MA.A.3.4.3
2	1.1 cont.	Cover Goal 2. You may also wish to take a little class time to discuss some of the more challenging patterns on SB pp. 2–3.	pp. 2–3 (after lesson)	MA.D.1.4.1, MA.D.2.4.1
3	1.2	Assign SB p. 4 as part of homework to prepare for the next lesson.		
4	1.3, Alg. Rev. p. 522, & SB p. 5	Cover Goal 1. Use Example 1 on p. 522 and the examples on SB p. 5 to review absolute value and radicals. Assign exercises on SB p. 5 as part of homework. You may also wish to assign some of Exs. 1–12 on p. 522.	p. 4 (before lesson) p. 5	MA.A.3.4.2, MA.A.3.4.3 MA.A.1.4.1, MA.A.1.4.4, MA.A.3.4.1
5	1.3 cont.	Cover Goal 2.		
6	1.4		pp. 6–7 (after lesson)	MA.A.1.4.4, MA.A.3.4.3, MA.B.1.4.2, MA.E.1.4.1
7	1.5 & SB p. 8	Review solving equations using SB and do pre-lesson activity. For additional material on solving simple linear equations, you may wish to use SRH p. 789 (all examples) and p. 790 (Example a only) and/or Alg. Rev. p. 258 (Example 3).	p. 8	MA.D.2.4.2
8	1.5 cont.	Cover instruction and examples in Goals 1 and 2, but omit both compass construction activities.	p. 9 (after lesson)	MA.C.3.4.2
9	1.6	Include pre-lesson tech activity.	See Days 24–25.	
10				

Module 1 *(continued)*

Day	Lesson Materials	Notes	Page(s) in Support Book (SB)	Benchmarks Covered in SB
11 12	1.7	You may wish to take a few minutes of class time to discuss Ex. 9 on SB pp. 10–11.	pp. 10–11 (after lesson)	MA.A.3.4.3, MA.B.1.4.1, MA.B.1.4.2, MA.B.2.4.2, MA.D.2.4.2
13	Ch. 2 Opener & SB pp. 12–13	Begin with Ch. 2 Opener on p. 69. Use *"Think & Discuss"* questions to lead in to a review of converting and estimating measures using SB. Note that the SB material on measurement is considered part of the assessed module content.	pp. 12–13	MA.B.2.4.1, MA.B.2.4.2, MA.B.3.4.1
14	Review			
15	Assess		pp. 14–15 (after test)	MA.A.2.4.2, MA.A.3.4.1, MA.A.3.4.2, MA.A.3.4.3

Module 1 Total—15 days   Remaining—153 days

Module 2 (Chapter 2) Reasoning and Proof

Day	Lesson Materials	Notes	Page(s) in Support Book (SB)	Benchmarks Covered in SB
16	2.1	Note that Ex. 3 on SB pp. 17–18 involves a conditional statement about data. You may wish to do this exercise together in class, perhaps as a replacement for Example 4.	pp. 17–18 (after lesson)	MA.E.1.4.2
17 18	2.2	You may wish to discuss the answers students found for Exs. 4–6 on SB pp. 17–18; these exercises deal with choosing when to use mean, median, mode, or range. Assign SB pp. 19–21 (listed with Days 19–20) as part of homework to prepare for the next lesson. (Note that additional material on the data topics in SB pp. 17–18, 19–21, including choosing measures of central tendency and working with misleading graphs, can be found in DAS 4.1, DAS 3.1, and DAS 3.2.)		

Module 2 *(continued)*

Day	Lesson Materials	Notes	Page(s) in Support Book (SB)	Benchmarks Covered in SB
19 20	2.3	Pre-lesson logic puzzle is optional. When you teach the difference between inductive and deductive reasoning in Example 3, you may wish to use SB pp. 19–21 for more examples; some conclusions in the SB are based on recognizing and extending patterns (see Exs. 4 & 8) and some are based on using the properties of the data display (see Examples 1–3, Exs. 2–3, 5–7). Assign SB p. 22 as part of homework to prepare for the next lesson.	pp. 19–21 (before lesson)	MA.E.1.4.1, MA.E.3.4.1
21	2.4	If your students need additional work on applying distributive property to simplify expressions or to solve equations, see SRH p. 787 and p. 790 (Example b) and/or Alg. Rev. p. 391.	p. 22 (before lesson) p. 23 (after lesson)	MA.A.2.4.2, MA.A.3.4.2, MA.A.3.4.3 MA.D.2.4.2
22 23	2.5	Include compass construction activity.	p. 24 (after lesson)	MA.A.1.4.2, MA.A.1.4.3, MA.A.1.4.4
24 25	2.6	Include pre-lesson Activity.	p. 25 (after 1.6 & 2.6)	MA.C.2.4.1
26	Review			
27	Assess		pp. 26–27 (after test)	MA.A.1.4.4, MA.A.3.4.1, MA.A.3.4.2, MA.A.3.4.3

Module 2 Total—12 days   Modules 1 and 2 Total—27 days   Remaining—141 days

Module 3 (Chapter 3) Perpendicular & Parallel Lines

Day	Lesson Materials	Notes	Page(s) in Support Book (SB)	Benchmarks Covered in SB
28	3.1	Omit compass construction activity.	p. 29 (after lesson)	MA.A.1.4.2, MA.A.1.4.3, MA.A.1.4.4, MA.A.3.4.1
29 30	3.2	Include pre-lesson activity.	p. 30 (after lesson)	MA.C.1.4.1
31 32	3.3	Include pre-lesson tech activity. Could be done by teacher in front of class.	p. 31 (after lesson)	MA.C.1.4.1
33	3.4		See Day 34	
34	3.5	Omit Goal 2 on compass constructions.	p. 32 (after 3.4 & 3.5)	MA.C.1.4.1, MA.C.2.4.1
35	3.6		pp. 33–34 (after lesson)	MA.B.2.4.2, MA.C.3.4.2, MA.D.1.4.2, MA.D.2.4.2,
36 37	3.7		p. 35 (after lesson)	MA.C.3.4.1, MA.C.3.4.2
38	Review			
39	Assess		pp. 36–37 (after test)	MA.E.1.4.1

Module 3 Total—12 days   Modules 1–3 Total—39 days   Remaining—129 days

Module 4 (Chapter 4 and part of Chapter 5) Recognizing and Applying Congruent Triangles

Day	Lesson Materials	Notes	Page(s) in Support Book (SB)	Benchmarks Covered in SB
40	4.1	Cover Goal 1 and then do pre-lesson activity.	p. 39 (after lesson)	MA.D.2.4.2
41	4.1 cont.	Cover Goal 2		
42	4.2		p. 40 (after lesson, correlates to 4.1)	MA.B.1.4.2, MA.C.2.4.1
43			Also see Day 46.	
44	4.3	Cover pre-lesson activity and Goal 1. Postpone compass construction activity.	See Day 46.	
45	4.3 cont.	Cover Goal 2		
46	4.4	Include post-lesson tech activity as teacher demo. Do on computer if available. Otherwise can do with ruler, compass, and protractor on overhead or on blackboard.	p. 41 (after 4.2, 4.3, & 4.4)	MA.B.2.4.1, MA.C.1.4.1, MA.C.2.4.1
47				
48	4.5	Omit Goal 2.	pp. 42–43 (after lesson)	MA.C.2.4.1
49	4.6	Include in-lesson activity.	p. 44 (after lesson)	MA.C.1.4.1, MA.C.2.4.1
50				
51	4.7		p. 45 (after lesson)	MA.C.3.4.1, MA.C.3.4.2
52				
53	5.1	Include pre-lesson activity. Omit compass construction activity. Postpone 5.2–5.4 to Module 12 after the FCAT. 5.5–5.6 will be covered in the next module.	p. 46 (after lesson)	MA.C.2.4.1
54				
55	Review			
56	Assess		pp. 47–48 (after test)	MA.D.2.4.2

Module 4 Total—17 days   Modules 1–4 Total—56 days   Remaining—112 days

Module 5 (Part of Chapter 5 and Chapter 6) Triangles and Quadrilaterals

Day	Lesson Materials	Notes	Page(s) in Support Book (SB)	Benchmarks Covered in SB
57 58	5.5 & SB pp. 50–51	Include pre-lesson tech activity. Could be done as teacher demo. If computer is not available, could instead be done with ruler and protractor, but finding measures will take longer. Spend some class time reviewing solving inequalities using SB. (For additional material on solving linear inequalities, you may wish to use SRH p. 791 and/or Alg. Rev. p. 259 (Example 4).)	pp. 50–51	MA.D.2.4.2
59 60	5.6		p. 52 (after lesson)	MA.C.1.4.1
61	6.1	To save time, omit pre-lesson activity and Example 2. (Example 2 will be covered instead in Module 8 with 11.1.)	pp. 53–54 (after lesson)	MA.B.1.4.2
62 63	6.2	Include pre-lesson tech activity.	See Days 64–65.	
64 65	6.3		p. 55 (after 6.2 & 6.3)	MA.C.1.4.1, MA.C.3.4.2
66 67	6.4		pp. 56–57 (after lesson) Also see Day 69.	MA.E.1.4.1
68	6.5	Omit Midsegment Theorem for trapezoids and Example 3. This will be covered in Module 12 after the FCAT.	See Day 69.	
69	6.6	Omit Example 2 since the proof relies on the Midsegment Theorem for triangles which is not covered until Module 12.	pp. 58–59 (after 6.4, 6.5, & 6.6)	MA.C.1.4.1, MA.C.3.4.1, MA.C.3.4.2
70	6.7	Cover pre-lesson activity and Goal 1. Could do activity as teacher demo to save time.		

Module 5 (continued)

Day	Lesson Materials	Notes	Page(s) in Support Book (SB)	Benchmarks Covered in SB
71	6.7 cont. & App. 3	Cover Goal 2. Use student help on p. 375 to lead in to the estimation work in App. 3. Cover Examples 1 & 2 of App. 3. Omit text between Theorems 6.23–6.25 and Example 4 on p. 374 and cover proof method in Ex. 58, rather than method in Ex. 59. Note that the material in App. 3 on estimating measures is considered part of the assessed module content.	pp. 60–61 (after 6.7 & App. 3)	MA.A.4.4.1, MA.B.1.4.1, MA.B.3.4.1
72	Review			
73	Assess	If your students need more practice with percent than is included on SB pp. 62–63, you may wish to also make use of the Alg. Rev. on p. 657. Percent of change will be reviewed on a separate SB sheet in Module 7.	pp. 62–63 (after test)	MA.A.1.4.3, MA.A.1.4.4, MA.A.3.4.3

Module 5 Total—17 days   Modules 1–5 Total—73 days   Remaining—95 days

Module 6 (Chapter 7) Transformations

Day	Lesson Materials	Notes	Page(s) in Support Book (SB)	Benchmarks Covered in SB
74	7.1	Include pre-lesson activity.		
75				
76	7.2	Include pre-lesson activity.	See Day 78.	
77				
78	7.3	Pre-lesson activity is optional. Omit proof of Theorem 7.2. Also omit Theorem 7.3 and Example 3. Cover in-lesson construction activity.	pp. 65–66 (after 7.2 & 7.3)	MA.C.2.4.1, MA.C.3.4.1
79	7.4	Omit Goal 2.	pp. 67–68 (after lesson)	MA.C.3.4.2
80	7.5	Include pre-lesson activity. Postpone 7.6 until Module 12 after the FCAT.	p. 69 (after 7.1–7.5)	MA.C.2.4.1, MA.C.3.4.1
81				
82	Review			
83	Assess	If your students need more practice with solving systems of equations than is included on SB pp. 70–71, you may also use SRH p. 796.	pp. 70–71 (after test)	MA.D.2.4.2

Module 6 Total—10 days   Modules 1–6 Total—83 days   Remaining—85 days

Module 7 (Chapter 8 and part of Chapter 9) Similarity

Day	Lesson Materials	Notes	Page(s) in Support Book (SB)	Benchmarks Covered in SB
84	8.1	Cover ratios and proportional reasoning with geometric figures using Examples 1–4 in 8.1		
85	8.1 cont. & 8.2	Cover properties of proportions and solving proportions using Examples 5–7 in 8.1 and Examples 1–2 in 8.2. Be sure to include some application problems.		
86	8.2 cont. & SB pp. 73–74	Use Example 4 in 8.2 and SB examples to focus on a variety of application problems, including estimation problems. Omit Geometric Mean and Example 3 in 8.2. Note that the SB material on proportional reasoning is considered part of the assessed module content.	pp. 73–74	MA.A.4.4.1, MA.B.1.4.3, MA.B.2.4.1, MA.B.3.4.1, MA.C.2.4.1, MA.C.3.4.1, MA.C.3.4.2, MA.E.1.4.3
87	8.3	Include pre-lesson activity.		
88				
89	8.4	Include in-lesson activity.	p. 75 (after lesson)	MA.B.2.4.1, MA.C.3.4.2
90				
91	8.5		p. 76 (after lesson)	MA.C.2.4.1
92				
93	8.6	Include pre-lesson activity. Can be done as demo in front of class. Omit compass construction activity. Assign SB p. 77 as part of homework to prepare for next lesson.		
94				
95	8.7	Postpone compass construction activity.	p. 77 (before lesson) p. 78 (after lesson)	MA.A.3.4.3 MA.C.2.4.1, MA.C.3.4.1
96	9.1	Include in-lesson activity. Postpone Goal 2.	p. 79 (after lesson)	MA.B.2.4.1, MA.C.2.4.1
97	Review			
98	Assess		pp. 80–81 (after test)	MA.E.3.4.1, MA.E.3.4.2

Module 7 Total—15 days   Modules 1–7 Total—98 days   Remaining—70 days

Module 8 (Chapters 9 and 11) Measures of Two-Dimensional Figures and Probability

Day	Lesson Materials	Notes	Page(s) in Support Book (SB)	Benchmarks Covered in SB
99	9.2 & SB p. 83	Spend some class time reviewing simplifying and comparing radicals using SB. You may also wish to use SRH p. 799 and Alg. Rev. pp. 522–523 (Examples 2 & 3). Introduce Pythagorean Theorem. Prove Theorem using method from Exs. 37 or 38 on p. 540 or method in Math and History on p. 557 rather than using method shown on p. 535.	p. 83	MA.A.1.4.2, MA.A.1.4.3, MA.A.1.4.4, MA.A.2.4.2, MA.A.3.4.1, MA.A.3.4.3
100	9.2 cont.	Cover Goal 2	p. 84 (after lesson)	MA.B.2.4.1
101 102	9.3		p. 85 (after lesson)	MA.C.2.4.1, MA.C.3.4.1
103 104	9.4	Include pre-lesson activity. Postpone 9.5–9.7 until Module 11 after the FCAT. Postpone Chapter 10 (except parts of 10.1 & 10.7 noted below) until Module 10 after the FCAT.	p. 86 (after lesson)	MA.D.1.4.1
105 106	6.1 & 11.1	Begin with definition of convex and concave polygons and Example 2 from 6.1. Include in-lesson activity in 11.1. You may wish to point out to students the connection with SB p. 86 that they did the previous night; when they do the activity they are actually continuing a function table and writing a rule for the function.	p. 87 (after lesson)	MA.B.1.4.2, MA.C.1.4.1
107	11.3	Cover pre-lesson activity and Goal 1.		

Module 8 *(continued)*

Day	Lesson Materials	Notes	Page(s) in Support Book (SB)	Benchmarks Covered in SB
108	11.3 cont. & parts of 10.1, 10.7, & 11.4	Spend 1/2 day on Goal 2 of 11.3. Spend other 1/2 day beginning work on circles. Introduce vocabulary in first four paragraphs of p. 595 in 10.1 (circle, center, radius, congruent circles, diameter). Use p. 642 in 10.7 to introduce idea of circle as locus of points and have teacher demonstrate drawing a circle with a compass. Students will use compass themselves when 10.7 is revisited in Module 11. Omit rest of 10.1 and 10.7. Then cover circumference formula and Example 1 in 11.4.	p. 88 (after 11.3)	MA.B.1.4.3, MA.C.2.4.1, MA.C.3.4.1
109	11.4 cont.	Cover remaining parts of 11.4.	p. 89 (after lesson)	MA.B.1.4.1, MA.B.1.4.2
110 111	11.5 & SB p. 90	Omit Example 4. As time permits, use SB for additional work on area of composite figures involving circles or sectors.	p. 90	MA.B.1.4.1
112	DAS 1.1, DAS 1.2, & SB p. 91	Review counting techniques using Examples 1 & 2 in DAS 1.1 and basic probability concepts using Examples 1 & 3 in DAS 1.2. Then apply these ideas to solve probability problems on SB p. 91. Note that basic probability ideas are considered part of the assessed module content.	p. 91	MA.E.2.4.1
113	11.6			
114	DAS 1.3	Cover probability of independent and dependent compound events using Examples 1–3 in DAS 1.3.	p. 92 (after DAS 1.3)	MA.E.2.4.2
115	Review			
116	Assess		p. 93 (after test)	MA.E.1.4.1

Module 8 Total—18 days   Modules 1–8 Total—116 days   Remaining—52 days

Module 9 (Chapter 12) Surface Area and Volume

Day	Lesson Materials	Notes	Page(s) in Support Book (SB)	Benchmarks Covered in SB
117	12.1	Cover p. 719 and Example 3. Omit Example 2 and Examples 4–6.	p. 95 (after lesson)	MA.C.2.4.2
118 119	12.2	Include pre-lesson activity. Omit Example 2b and Exs. 22, 23, 25, 30, 36, 37, 44 since area of a regular polygon was postponed until Module 11 after the FCAT.	See Days 120–121.	
120 121	12.3	Omit Example 2. Instead go through an example of finding the surface area of a square pyramid. This could be done using the pyramid shown for Extra Example 1 in the TE side column. Also omit Exs. 18, 19, 28, 29, 37, 47–49.	p. 96 (after 12.2 & 12.3)	MA.B.1.4.1
122	12.4	Omit Exs. 15, 21, 31, 44.	See Days 123–124.	
123 124	12.5	Include pre-lesson activity. Omit Examples 1 and 4 and Exs. 6, 10, 13–16, 22, 30, since area of a regular polygon was postponed until Module 11 after the FCAT. Instead of current Example 1, you could find the volume of a square pyramid with base side lengths of 3 cm and height of 4 cm. (Alternatively, you could find the area of the base in current Example 1 by first using the Pythagorean Theorem to find the height of one of the six equilateral triangles.) Omit 12.6.	p. 97 (after 12.4 & 12.5)	MA.B.1.4.1
125 126	12.7	Omit Example 4 and Exs. 8, 23, 28, 31–33, 36, 37.	p. 98 (after lesson)	MA.B.1.4.3, MA.C.2.4.1, MA.D.1.4.2
127	Review			
128	Assess			

Module 9 Total—12 days   Modules 1–9 Total—128 days   Remaining—40 days

AFTER THE FCAT

Module 10 (Chapter 10) Circles

Day	Lesson Materials	Notes
129	10.1	Begin with the new vocabulary on p. 595 that was not already covered in Module 8 (chord, secant, and tangent).
130		
131	10.2	
132		
133	10.3	
134		
135	10.4	
136	10.5	
137		
138	10.6	
139	10.7	Revisit the idea of a circle as a locus of points that was introduced briefly in Module 8. Cover the entire lesson now. Use ruler, compass, and/or protractor as appropriate to draw figures.
140		
141	Review	
142	Assess	

Module 10 Total—14 days   Modules 1–10 Total—142 days   Remaining—26 days

Module 11 (Chapter 9 and parts of Chapters 11 and 12) Right Triangles and Trigonometry

Day	Lesson Materials	Notes
143	parts of 8.2, 9.1, & 9.2	Cover the definition of geometric mean and Example 3 in 8.2. Next cover Goal 2 in 9.1. Then cover the proof of the Pythagorean Theorem using a Geometric Mean Theorem on p. 535 in 9.2.
144		
145	9.5	
146		
147	9.6	
148	9.7	
149		
150	11.2 & parts of 12.2–12.5	Cover 11.2. Then revisit 12.2–12.5 and apply area of a regular polygon to find surface area and volume of prisms and pyramids with triangular or hexagonal bases. Cover Example 2b in 12.2, Example 2 in 12.3, and Example 1 or 4 in 12.5. Include some surface area and volume exercises from 12.2–12.5 in the homework.
151		
152	Review	
153	Assess	

Module 11 Total—11 days   Modules 1–11 Total—153 days   Remaining—15 days

Module 12 (Various chapters) Constructions, Triangle Relationships, and Other Topics

Day	Lesson Materials	Notes
154	parts of 1.5, 3.1, 3.5, 4.3, & 4.5	Cover compass constructions in 1.5, 3.1, 3.5, 4.3. Cover Goal 2 in 4.5.
155		
156	5.1 & 5.2	Cover the compass construction in 5.1. Cover entire lesson 5.2.
157		
158	5.3	
159		
160	5.4	
161		
162	parts of 6.5, 6.6, & 6.7	Cover Midsegment Theorem for trapezoids and Example 3 in 6.5. Cover Example 2 in 6.6. Then use 6.7 to make the connection between the Midsegment Theorem for trapezoids and the area of a trapezoid. Go over the Student Help note and text above Example 4 on p. 374 and use the method in Ex. 59 to prove the area formula.
163	7.3	Cover proof of Theorem 7.2 in Example 1. Then cover Theorem 7.3 and Example 3.
164	7.4	Cover Goal 2 only. Goal 1 was covered in Module 6.
165	12.1	Cover Examples 2 and 4–6.
166	12.6	If you have time, you may also wish to cover Example 4 from 12.7.
167	Review	
168	Assess	

Module 12 Total—15 days   Modules 1–12 Total—168 days   Remaining—0 days

Correlation to Florida Benchmarks

Benchmark	Diagnostic Test Exercises	Support Book Pages
MA.A.1.4.1	Ex. 3	5
MA.A.1.4.2	Ex. 12	24, 29, 83
MA.A.1.4.3	Ex. 12	1, 24, 29, 62–63, 83
MA.A.1.4.4	Exs. 3, 12	5, 6–7, 24, 26–27, 29, 62–63, 83
MA.A.2.4.2	Exs. 3, 21	1, 14–15, 22, 83
MA.A.3.4.1	Exs. 3, 47	1, 5, 14–15, 26–27, 29, 83
MA.A.3.4.2	Exs. 4, 21	4, 14–15, 22, 26–27
MA.A.3.4.3	Exs. 19, 34	1, 4, 6–7, 10–11, 14–15, 22, 26–27, 62–63, 77, 83
MA.A.4.4.1	Ex. 31	60–61, 73–74
MA.B.1.4.1	Exs. 23, 25, 36, 39, 40, 41, 42, 44, 50	10–11, 60–61, 89, 90, 96, 97
MA.B.1.4.2	Exs. 18, 38	6–7, 10–11, 40, 53–54, 87, 89
MA.B.1.4.3	Exs. 5, 33	73–74, 88, 98
MA.B.2.4.1	Exs. 5, 33, 48	12–13, 41, 73–74, 75, 79, 84
MA.B.2.4.2	Ex. 18	10–11, 12–13, 33–34
MA.B.3.4.1	Ex. 18	12–13, 60–61, 73–74
MA.C.1.4.1	Exs. 6, 7, 8, 9, 13, 24, 26, 32, 40, 51, 52	30, 31, 32, 41, 44, 52, 55, 58–59, 87
MA.C.2.4.1	Exs. 2, 6, 7, 8, 9, 10, 13, 20, 22, 24, 26, 29, 30, 32, 33, 36, 40, 44, 45, 48, 49, 51, 52	25, 32, 40, 41, 42–43, 44, 46, 65–66, 69, 73–74, 76, 78, 79, 85, 88, 98
MA.C.2.4.2	Ex. 42	95
MA.C.3.4.1	Exs. 5, 14, 28, 30, 48	35, 45, 58–59, 65–66, 69, 73–74, 78, 85, 88
MA.C.3.4.2	Exs. 5, 11, 14, 19, 46, 52	9, 33–34, 35, 45, 55, 58–59, 67–68, 73–74, 75
MA.D.1.4.1	Exs. 1, 43	2–3, 86
MA.D.1.4.2	Ex. 16	33–34, 98
MA.D.2.4.1	Exs. 1, 37	2–3
MA.D.2.4.2	Exs. 6, 8, 10, 21, 22, 27	8, 10–11, 23, 33–34, 39, 47–48, 50–51, 70–71
MA.E.1.4.1	Exs. 17, 37	6–7, 19–21, 36–37, 56–57, 93
MA.E.1.4.2	Ex. 15	17–18
MA.E.1.4.3	Ex. 31	73–74

Benchmark	Diagnostic Test Exercises	Support Book Pages
MA.E.2.4.1	Ex. 35	91
MA.E.2.4.2	Ex. 35	92
MA.E.3.4.1	Exs. 17, 37	19–21, 80–81
MA.E.3.4.2	Ex. 17	80–81

About the FCAT

The Florida Comprehensive Assessment Test (FCAT) is designed to promote the effectiveness of teaching and learning in Florida's public schools. The test is given to all public school students in Grades 3–10. Student knowledge of the Sunshine State Standards is measured by the FCAT.

THE FIVE MATHEMATICAL STRANDS

The FCAT for mathematics contains questions from five content areas:

A. Number Sense, Concepts, and Operations
B. Measurement
C. Geometry and Spatial Sense
D. Algebraic Thinking
E. Data Analysis and Probability

TYPES OF QUESTIONS

The FCATs in mathematics for Grades 6–10 include multiple-choice and gridded-response questions. The Grade 8 and Grade 10 tests also include short-response items, which are graded using a two-point scale, and extended-response items, which are graded using a four-point scale. All questions are presented as word problems.

It is recommended that students spend about 1 minute on each multiple-choice question, 1.5 minutes on each gridded-response question, 3–5 minutes on each short-response question, and 5–15 minutes on each extended-response question.

Students in Grades 7–10 taking the FCAT for mathematics are permitted to use four-function calculators. However, students in Grade 6 may not use calculators.

Gridded-response, short-response, and extended-response questions are labeled with symbols in the test book, as shown below.

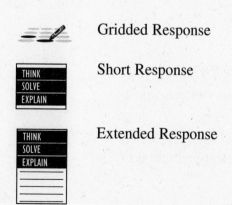

Gridded Response

Short Response

Extended Response

How to Prepare for the FCAT

The best way to prepare for any test is to be an active learner throughout the year. Try not to fall behind in class. If you keep up in class, and you practice some simple test-taking strategies, you should feel more confident when you take the FCAT for mathematics.

BEFORE THE TEST

Keep up with the material in class. Complete the homework assignments carefully and consistently. When you do each homework assignment, make a list of questions to ask in class if there are points that you do not understand.

Review your notes and the class materials every day to be certain that you understand the important terms and concepts of that day's lesson.

Take a sample test, if possible, or complete sample test problems to become familiar with the test and to identify any areas in which you need more practice.

THE NIGHT BEFORE THE TEST

The night before the test, try to relax and review your strategies for taking the test.

Avoid last-minute cramming. Review the material the night before the test, but don't try to learn weeks of new material.

Review the symbols for the different types of questions on the FCAT for mathematics. (See page H1.)

Stay positive. Try to spend the evening in a good mood and try not to worry. Remember that the test is an opportunity to show what you have learned.

Gather your supplies. Put your pencils (with erasers), watch, glasses (if you use them), and other necessary supplies in one place.

Get a good night's sleep!

THE DAY OF THE TEST

Have a good breakfast. Don't overeat or try something new.

Dress comfortably. You might want to dress in layers so you can adjust your clothing to the temperature in the testing room.

Arrive early. Choose a comfortable spot. If you feel anxious, take several deep breaths to help yourself relax and tell yourself you will do your best.

DURING THE TEST

1. Read the instructions. Listen carefully to any directions given by the person supervising the test.

2. Preview the test. Decide which problems you will do first. Some people prefer to start with short, easy questions. Others like to do the longer, more difficult questions first.

3. Budget your time. Remember that the FCAT is a timed test, so avoid spending too much time on any one question.

4. Make notes, sketches, and calculations in the white space of your test book to help you solve problems, but record your answers neatly in your answer book. Be sure to answer all parts of the short-response and extended-response questions completely.

5. Check for careless errors, like switching two numbers or misplacing a decimal point.

6. Check that your answers are reasonable. For example, if a question asks for a distance, the answer should be positive.

7. It is best to try to answer all the questions on the test. There is no penalty for guessing on the FCAT.

8. If you get stuck, move on. Put a mark next to an unanswered question in your test book so you can find it faster if you go back to it later. If you do skip a question, be sure to skip it in your answer book as well.

9. Use all the available time. If you finish early, go back and double-check as many answers as you can.

10. Think positively during the test. Focus on each question as you work on it.

11. Don't worry about what other students are doing on the test. This will only distract you. Work at the pace that is right for you.

12. If you become tense and worried, stop and take several deep breaths. This will help you feel calmer so you can concentrate on the test.

13. If you feel distracted while reading a multiple-choice question, cover the multiple choice answers with a piece of paper or your hand until you are ready.

14. Read all the answer choices to multiple-choice questions carefully before answering. Be careful about choosing an answer that seems obvious.

15. Eliminate any answer choices that are clearly incorrect. For example, if a question asks for an area, eliminate any answers that don't involve square units.

16. If you don't know which answer choice is correct, you may be able to work backward. Try testing the answers to see if they work.

Solving Word Problems

All FCAT questions are presented as word problems. In addition, the Grade 8 and Grade 10 FCATs for mathematics include short-response and extended-response questions, for which you are expected to write complete solutions. Below are some tips to help you read and solve word problems.

HOW TO READ A WORD PROBLEM

Before you can solve a word problem, you need to read and understand it.

- Read it once quickly to understand the main ideas and identify the question being asked.

- Read it carefully a second time before starting a solution. Underline important information, cross out unnecessary information, and begin to think about your answer.

- Make a sketch, a graph, or a table in the white space of your test book to help you organize the information. Do not write on the answer sheet yet.

HOW TO SOLVE A WORD PROBLEM

After you have carefully read a word problem, then you can work toward a solution. Remember not to spend too much time on any one question.

- Come up with a plan to solve the problem. You might want to use formulas, conversions, graphs, diagrams, or tables as part of the solution or to find the solution. If graphs, diagrams, or tables are part of the solution to a short- or extended-response question, make and label them carefully in your answer book.

- Carry out your plan to find the solution. Watch out for careless errors such as misplacing a decimal point or using the wrong operation. Show all your work in the answer book for short- and extended-response questions.

- Make sure you answered the question being asked. Be sure to check all of your work, not just your final answer.

- If the question is multiple choice or gridded response, make sure you filled out the answer sheet correctly and completely.

- If the question is short response or extended response, the work that you include in your responses shows that you understand how to solve the problem. Try to show your work even if you're not sure of the final answer, because you may receive partial credit.

ANSWERING SHORT-RESPONSE QUESTIONS

Short-response questions are scored using a two-point system. A full credit, two-point solution indicates that the student has a solid understanding of the concepts introduced in the question, has shown and completed all work correctly, and has provided sound reasoning to explain the answer. Here is an example of a short-response question and a full credit solution.

Sample Question

A photographer charges $125 for a portrait sitting, plus a fee for each print made. A client has a sitting and orders 4 prints. The total fee is $300.

Part A Write an equation that could be used to find the number of prints ordered. Let p be the cost of one print.

Part B Determine the cost per print. Show all your work.

Full Credit Solution

Part A Let p = the cost of one print.
The cost of 4 prints is $4p$.
The charge for the sitting is $125.
The total fee is $300.
So, the cost of four prints plus the charge for the sitting equals the total fee.

Equation $4p + 125 = 300$

Part B To determine the cost per print, solve the equation
$4p + 125 = 300$ for p.

$$4p + 125 = 300$$
$$4p = 175$$
$$p = 43.75$$

The cost of one print is $43.75.

Cost per print $43.75

A **partial credit,** one-point solution may indicate that the student has a good understanding of the concepts introduced in the question, but has not shown or completed all work correctly, and may not have provided sound reasoning to explain the answer. It also may indicate that the student has given a correct answer, but has arrived at that answer without a solid understanding of the concepts introduced in the question or has not provided appropriate reasoning.

In the sample solution below, the answer to *Part A* is correct, but the reasoning is not shown. The answer to *Part B* is incorrect due to a miscalculation in the second step (the student added 125 to each side instead of subtracting). However, the student showed all work in *Part B*. Therefore, this is a partial credit solution.

Partial Credit Solution

Part A   Let p = the cost of one print.
The equation is $4p + 125 = 300$.

Equation $4p + 125 = 300$

Part B $4p + 125 = 300$
$$4p = 425$$
$$p = 106.25$$

The cost of one print is $106.25.
Cost per print $106.25

A **no credit,** zero-point solution indicates that the student has no understanding of the concepts introduced in the question, has not shown or completed the work correctly, and has not provided sound reasoning to explain the answer. A Student will receive no credit for providing no response at all, so try to show your work even if you are not sure of the final answer, because you may receive partial credit.

In the sample solution below, there is no reasoning, no work, and no answer shown for *Part A*. Because there is nothing written, there is no possibility for points to be awarded. That is why you should attempt to answer questions, if time permits, even if you don't know the answer. There is no reasoning shown and the answer is incorrect for *Part B*. Therefore, this is a no credit solution.

No Credit Solution

Part A

Equation _____

Part B $300 \div 4 = \$75$

Cost per print $\$75$

ANSWERING EXTENDED-RESPONSE QUESTIONS

Extended-response questions are scored using a four-point system. The general criteria used for grading an extended-response question are the same as those used for grading a short-response question. A full credit solution is worth four points, a partial credit solution is worth one to three points, and a no credit solution is worth zero points. Here is an example of an extended-response question and a full credit solution.

Sample Question

$\triangle ABD$ and $\triangle ECD$ are similar.

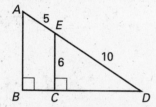

Part A   Explain in words why $\triangle ABD$ is similar to $\triangle ECD$.

Part B   Write a proportion that could be used to find the length of $\overline{AB}$.

Part C   Solve the proportion in **Part B** to determine the length of $\overline{AB}$. Show your work.

Full Credit Solution

Part A $\angle B$ and $\angle ECD$ are both right angles, so they are congruent. $\angle D$ is congruent to itself. Two angles of $\triangle ABD$ are congruent to two angles of $\triangle ECD$, so the triangles are similar.

Part B   Because corresponding lengths in similar triangles are in proportion, I can write the following proportion:

Proportion $\dfrac{AB}{EC} = \dfrac{AD}{ED}$

Part C $AD = AE + ED = 5 + 10 = 15$

$$\frac{AB}{EC} = \frac{AD}{ED}$$

$$\frac{AB}{6} = \frac{15}{10}$$

$$AB = \frac{15}{10} \times 6$$

$$AB = 9$$

Length of $\overline{AB}$ _____9_____

In the sample solution below, the reasoning for *Part A* is incomplete. The proportion set up in *Part B* is wrong, but the reasoning is correct. The answer to *Part C* is incorrect because it is dependent on the answer to *Part B*. However, both the work and the reasoning are shown for *Part C*. Therefore, this is a partial credit solution.

Partial Credit Solution

Part A $\angle A$ and $\angle CED$ are congruent because of the parallel lines. $\angle D$ is congruent to itself. Two angles of $\triangle ABD$ are congruent to two angles of $\triangle ECD$, so the triangles are similar.

Part B Because corresponding lengths in similar triangles are in proportion:

Proportion $\dfrac{AB}{EC} = \dfrac{AE}{ED}$

Part C $\dfrac{AB}{EC} = \dfrac{AE}{ED}$

$\dfrac{AB}{6} = \dfrac{5}{10}$

$AB = \dfrac{5}{10} \times 6$

$AB = 3$

Length of $\overline{AB}$ ____3____

In the sample solution below, the answers to all three parts are wrong. Also, there is no reasoning or work shown for any of the parts. Therefore, this is a no credit solution.

No Credit Solution

Part A The triangles are similar because one is smaller than the other.

Part B **Proportion** $\dfrac{AB}{EC} = \dfrac{AE}{ED}$

Part C $\dfrac{AB}{AC} = \dfrac{AE}{ED}$

Length of $\overline{AB}$ ____8____

Gridded-Response Questions

Gridded-response questions on the FCAT for mathematics are labeled with the symbol at the right. Answers for gridded-response questions are completed on a response grid like the one shown below.

PARTS OF A RESPONSE GRID

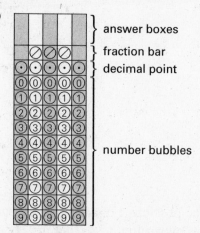

answer boxes
fraction bar
decimal point
number bubbles

There may be more than one correct answer to a gridded-response question and more than one way to complete a response grid. When writing your answer in the answer boxes, it is a good idea to start in the leftmost column. By starting in the leftmost column, you don't have to think about how many columns you will need to fit your entire answer.

ANSWERING A GRIDDED-RESPONSE QUESTION

1. **Solve the problem** Solve the problem carefully and check your answer before completing the response grid.

2. **Fill in the answer boxes** Print your answer in the answer boxes provided at the top of the response grid.

   • Write the first digit of your answer in the leftmost answer box, OR write the last digit in the rightmost answer box. (Remember that starting in the left column is recommended.)

   • Each answer box should contain only one digit or symbol. NEVER leave a blank answer box in the middle of an answer.

   • If necessary, include a decimal point or a fraction bar in the answer box.

3. **Fill in the bubbles** Fill in a bubble under each digit or symbol you wrote in the answer boxes.

   • There should be only one bubble filled in per answer box. NEVER fill in a bubble under a blank answer box. Leave the bubbles in that column empty.

   • You MUST fill in the bubbles that correspond to an answer box completely and accurately with a solid black mark in order to receive credit.

   • If you need to erase an answer, erase it completely, because stray marks may be read incorrectly by the scoring machine.

EXAMPLES

Whole numbers Work from the left, so you don't have to think about how many spaces you will need. Leave unused columns blank.

$4 \times 16 =$

Decimals Enter the most accurate value possible. For example, if your answer is 3.333..., use all the spaces on the grid by writing 3.333, not just 3.3.

$0.000425 \times 10^3 =$

Fractions Mixed numbers *cannot* be written in the answer grid. If your answer is a mixed number, you must rewrite it as an improper fraction or as a decimal.

If you try to fill in $6\frac{3}{8}$, it will be read as $\frac{63}{8}$ and will be counted wrong.

INCORRECT

$3\frac{7}{8} + 2\frac{1}{2} =$

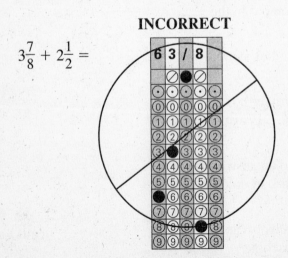

CORRECT

$$3\frac{7}{8} + 2\frac{1}{2} =$$

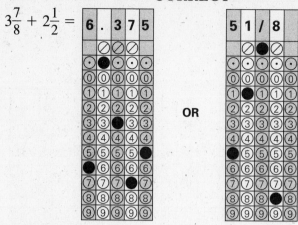

OR

Multiple Answers Some answers may be a range of values. If this is the case, you can grid the answer in different ways.

For the inequality $x > 3.5$ and $x < 4.1$, you can write any of the following answers.

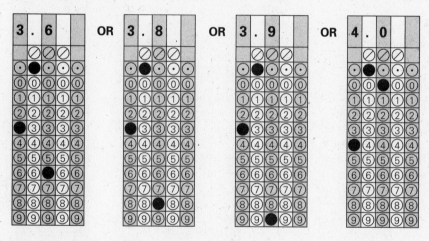

There are many other correct answers.

Name _____ Date _____

Gridding Sheet

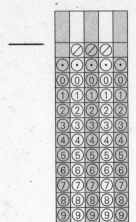   

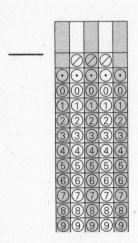   

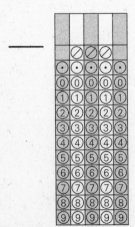   

FCAT MATHEMATICS REFERENCE SHEET

Area

 Triangle $A = \frac{1}{2}bh$

 Rectangle $A = lw$

 Trapezoid $A = \frac{1}{2}h(b_1 + b_2)$

 Parallelogram $A = bh$

 Circle $A = \pi r^2$

Key

b = base d = diameter
h = height r = radius
l = length A = area
w = width C = circumference
ℓ = slant height V = volume
$S.\,A.$ = surface area

Use 3.14 or $\frac{22}{7}$ for π.

Circumference

$$C = \pi d = 2\pi r$$

	Volume	Total Surface Area
Right Circular Cone	$V = \frac{1}{3}\pi r^2 h$	$S.A. = \frac{1}{2}(2\pi r)\ell + \pi r^2 = \pi r \ell + \pi r^2$
Square Pyramid	$V = \frac{1}{3}lwh$	$S.A. = 4\left(\frac{1}{2}l\ell\right) + l^2 = 2l\ell + l^2$
Sphere	$V = \frac{4}{3}\pi r^3$	$S.A. = 4\pi r^2$
Right Circular Cylinder	$V = \pi r^2 h$	$S.A. = 2\pi rh + 2\pi r^2$
Rectangular Solid	$V = lwh$	$S.A. = 2(lw) + 2(hw) + 2(lh)$

In the following formulas, n represents the number of sides:

In a polygon, the sum of the measures of the interior angles is equal to $180(n - 2)$.

In a regular polygon, the measure of an interior angle is equal to $\frac{180(n - 2)}{n}$.

FCAT MATHEMATICS REFERENCE SHEET

Pythagorean Theorem

$$c^2 = a^2 + b^2$$

Distance between two points
$P_1(x_1, y_1)$ and $P_2(x_2, y_2)$:

$$\sqrt{(x_2 - x_1)^2 + (y_2 - y_1)^2}$$

$$y = mx + b$$

Slope-intercept form of an equation of a line, where m = slope and b = the y-intercept.

Midpoint between two points
$P_1(x_1, y_1)$ and $P_2(x_2, y_2)$:

$$\left(\frac{x_2 + x_1}{2}, \frac{y_2 + y_1}{2} \right)$$

$$d = rt$$

Distance, rate, time formula, where
d = distance, r = rate, t = time

$$I = prt$$

Simple interest formula, where
p = principal, r = rate, t = time

Conversions

1 yard = 3 feet = 36 inches
1 mile = 1760 yards = 5280 feet
1 acre = 43,560 square feet

1 hour = 60 minutes
1 minute = 60 seconds

1 liter = 1000 milliliters = 1000 cubic centimeters
1 meter = 100 centimeters = 1000 millimeters
1 kilometer = 1000 meters
1 gram = 1000 milligrams
1 kilogram = 1000 grams

1 cup = 8 fluid ounces
1 pint = 2 cups
1 quart = 2 pints
1 gallon = 4 quarts

1 pound = 16 ounces
1 ton = 2000 pounds

Metric numbers with four digits are presented without a comma (e.g. 9960 kilometers). For metric numbers greater than four digits, a space is used instead of a comma (e.g. 12 500 liters).

Name _____ Date _____

Integers

Support for Benchmarks MA.A.1.4.3, MA.A.2.4.2, MA.A.3.4.1, MA.A.3.4.3

EXAMPLES

Which is greater, $10(-10)$ or $(-10)^2$?

Solution

A positive number times a negative number is negative.
$10(-10) = -100$

A negative number times a negative number is positive.
$(-10)^2 = (-10)(-10)$
$\quad\quad\quad = 100$

Because $-100 < 100$, $10(-10) < (-10)^2$.

The square on the number line represents the number 5. The star shows the result of adding an integer to 5. What integer was added to 5?

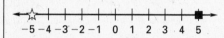

Solution

$5 + x = -5$
$\quad x = -5 - 5$
$\quad x = -5 + (-5)$
$\quad x = -10$

Therefore, -10 was added to 5 to get -5.

The temperature in Krakow is -5 degrees Celsius. The temperature in Vienna is -2 degrees Celsius. How many degrees colder is it in Krakow than in Vienna?

Solution

This question asks for the difference between -5 and -2.

$-5 - (-2)$
$\quad = -5 + 2$
$\quad = -3$

It is 3 degrees colder in Krakow than in Vienna.

Exercises

1. The number 2 is shown on the number line.

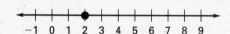

Which of the following number lines shows the value of 2 to the third power, or 2 cubed?

(A) ![number line A]   (C) ![number line C]

(B) ![number line B]   (D) ![number line D]

2. Where would -110 fall on a number line?

(F) to the left of -100 (H) between 0 and 100

(G) between -100 and 0   (I) to the right of 100

3. Tallahassee's elevation is 55 feet above sea level. The lowest parts of New Orleans lie 10 feet below sea level. What is the difference between the elevation of Tallahassee and the elevation of the lowest parts of New Orleans?

(A) 70.5 feet   (B) 65 feet   (C) 60.5 feet   (D) 45 feet

Copy and complete with >, <, or =.

4. $18 \div (-3) \underline{\ ?\ } -4 - (-9)$ **5.** $(-4)^2 \underline{\ ?\ } (-3)^2$ **6.** $-12 + (-8) \underline{\ ?\ } -8 - 12$

Patterns

Support for Benchmarks MA.D.1.4.1, MA.D.2.4.1

EXAMPLES The graph shows how much apples cost per pound. If the pattern is continued, how much do 5 pounds of apples cost?

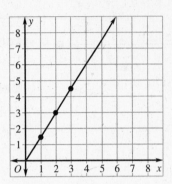

The cost goes up by $1.50 per pound. Five pounds of apples cost $7.50.

What is the next number in this sequence?

0.5, 4, 0.0625, 256, ____

The numbers follow a pattern. Each number in the sequence is the previous number raised to a power of -2.

$$(0.5)^{-2} = \frac{1}{(0.5)^2} = 4, \ 4^{-2} = \frac{1}{4^2}$$
$$= 0.0625,$$

$$(0.0625)^{-2} = \frac{1}{(0.0625)^2} = 256$$

The next number in the sequence is $256^{-2} \approx 0.0000153$.

A wallpaper border has the following pattern:

boat   train   plane   car   boat

Which figure will be eighth in the border?

The pattern repeats after four figures. The fourth figure is a car. When the position of a figure is a multiple of 4, the figure will be a car. So, the eighth figure will be a car.

Exercises

1. Diego is laying tile starting in one corner of a room. Every few minutes he adds one row of tile to each of the two open sides, according to the pattern shown below.

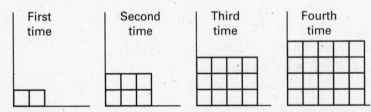

What will be the dimensions of the tile after Diego lays tiles for the eighth time?

(A) 10 tiles by 12 tiles

(B) 9 tiles by 10 tiles

(C) 8 tiles by 9 tiles

(D) 7 tiles by 8 tiles

Patterns *(continued)*

Support for Benchmarks MA.D.1.4.1, MA.D.2.4.1

2. Which BEST describes the pattern in the sequence of numbers below?

$$0.7, \ 0.49, \ 0.2401, \ 0.057648$$

   (F) Each number is the square of the previous number in the sequence.

   (G) Multiply a given number by 0.7 to find the next number in the sequence.

   (H) Raising a given number to the $\frac{1}{2}$ power results in the next number in the sequence.

   (I) To find the next number in the sequence, multiply the last number in the sequence by the previous number.

3. What is the next number in this sequence?

$$3.5, \ 5.25, \ 7.875, \ 11.8125, \ \underline{\quad}$$

4. Louisa is weaving a striped blanket according to the pattern below. The pattern uses abbreviations for the different colors: RD is red, NY is navy blue, LB is light blue, and WE is white.

    RD NY WE NY LB WE LB RD WE RD NY WE ___

What color will the next row be?

   (A) red   (C) light blue

   (B) navy blue   (D) white

5. The graph at the right shows the cost of *x* pounds of apples.

Assuming that the pattern of costs continues, what is the cost of 7 pounds of apples?

6. The first three objects in a pattern are shown. How many blocks are in the next object?

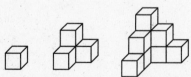

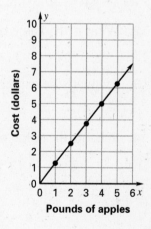

7. Keiko is a freelance computer technician who goes to her clients' homes or businesses. She charges her clients $20 for each visit and $30 for each hour of work.

   Part A Make a table that shows Keiko's charges after 1, 2, 3, 4, and 5 hours of work during one visit. Then write a rule that gives Keiko's charges after *x* hours of work.

   Part B Make a graph that shows Keiko's charges over time.

Order of Operations

Support for Benchmarks MA.A.3.4.2, MA.A.3.4.3

The **order of operations** is as follows:

1. Evaluate expressions in parentheses.
2. Evaluate exponential expressions, or powers.
3. Multiply and divide.
4. Add and subtract.

Always move from left to right when performing similar operations.

EXAMPLES

What is the value of the expression $(3 + 2)^2 - 15 \div 3$?

$(3 + 2)^2 - 15 \div 3$

$(5)^2 - 15 \div 3$ Evaluate parentheses.
                $3 + 2 = 5$

$25 - 15 \div 3$ Evaluate powers.
                $5^2 = 25$

$25 - 5$ Divide. $15 \div 3 = 5$

20 Subtract.
                $25 - 5 = 20$

The formula for the surface area of a cylinder is $S = 2(\pi r^2) + (2\pi r)h$. If $r = 4$ and $h = 8$, what is the surface area of the cylinder? Express your answer in terms of π.

$S = 2(\pi r^2) + (2\pi r)h$

$S = 2(\pi(4)^2) + (2\pi(4))8$ Substitute.

$S = 2(16\pi) + (2\pi(4))8$ Evaluate powers.

$S = 32\pi + 64\pi$ Multiply.

$S = 96\pi$ Add.

Exercises

1. Which of the following is the solution to the equation $n = 5(4 + 3) - 1$?

(A) 34   (B) 28   (C) 22   (D) 18

2. What is the value of the following expression?

$$3^3 - 2^2 + 5 \cdot 4$$

3. Evaluate the expression $(11 - 7)^2 + 3^2$.

(F) 25   (G) 14   (H) 3   (I) -29

4. What is the value of the following expression?

$$15 \cdot 12 - 4^3$$

5. Tina is solving the following equation.

$$y = 5^2 + 2(5) - 8$$

What is the **very next** operation she should perform after she squares 5?

(A) Subtract 8 from the square of 5.   (C) Subtract 8 from 5.

(B) Multiply 2 by 5.   (D) Divide 2 by 5.

6. What is the value of y if $x = 4$ in the following equation?

$$y = 3(x - 1)^2 + x \div 2 - 2$$

Name _____ Date _____

Representing Numbers

Support for Benchmarks MA.A.1.4.1, MA.A.1.4.4, MA.A.3.4.1

EXAMPLES Find the two square roots of 36:
$\sqrt{36}$ and $-\sqrt{36}$.

$6 \cdot 6 = 36$ and $-6 \cdot -6 = 36$

So, $\sqrt{36} = 6$ and $-\sqrt{36} = -6$.

Which of the following is equivalent to the expression $12x + |-34| - 2$?

(A) $12x - 36$ (C) $4(3x + 8)$

(B) $12x + 36$ (D) $12(x - 3)$

$12x + 34 - 2$	Find the absolute value.
$12x + 32$	Subtract.
$4(3x + 8)$	Factor.

The answer is C.

Reese is using the equation below to find the length, in centimeters, of side c of a triangle.

$$c^2 = (12 - 7)^2 + 12^2$$

What is the length of side c?

$c^2 = (12 - 7)^2 + 12^2$	
$c^2 = (5)^2 + 12^2$	Evaluate parenthetical expressions.
$c^2 = 25 + 144$	Evaluate powers.
$c^2 = 169$	Add.
$c = \sqrt{169}$	Take the positive square root of both sides of the equation.
$c = 13$ centimeters	

Exercises

1. Which of the following is equivalent to the expression $|-8| + 3^2$?

(A) absolute value of negative 8 plus 3 squared

(B) absolute value of negative 8 plus radical 3

(C) square root of negative 8 plus 3 squared

(D) radical negative 8 plus 3 times 2

2. Which of the following BEST describes the value of $\sqrt{33}$?

(F) between 5.8 and 6.0   (H) between 5.3 and 5.5

(G) between 5.5 and 5.8   (I) between 5.0 and 5.3

3. Evaluate the expression below.

$$\sqrt{6.25} + 3(10 - 7.5)^2$$

4. Using the Pythagorean Theorem, Marisol found that a building was $\sqrt{800}$ feet tall. Which of the following is equivalent to this value?

(A) 400 feet   (B) 80 feet   (C) $20\sqrt{2}$ feet   (D) $2\sqrt{20}$ feet

5. Evaluate $\sqrt{23^2}$.

6. Which of the following expressions is equivalent to y multiplied by the absolute value of 6?

(F) $|6y|$ (G) $|6|y$ (H) $\sqrt{6y}$ (I) $\sqrt{6}y$

Circles, Graphs, and Angles

Support for Benchmarks MA.A.1.4.4. MA.A.3.4.3, MA.B.1.4.2, MA.E.1.4.1

EXAMPLE 1 The graph shows the results of a survey that asked tenth graders to name their favorite type of music.

What percent of tenth graders did not find their favorite type of music listed and selected "Other"?

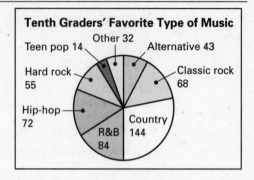

Tenth Graders' Favorite Type of Music

The percent of students who selected "Other" is the number of students who selected "Other" divided by the total number of students surveyed.

$\dfrac{32}{512} = 0.0625$ or 6.25%

EXAMPLE 2 Perkins Orchard grows a variety of citrus fruits. Limes make up 20% of the orchard's crop. If the Perkins Orchard crops were displayed in a circle graph, what would the angle measure for the lime section be?

A circle has 360 degrees. Limes make up 20% of the circle graph.

$360 \cdot 20\% = 360 \cdot 0.2 = 72$

So, the angle measure for the lime section would be 72 degrees.

Exercises

1. The data in the table will be displayed in a circle graph.

What will be the angle measure for the section of the circle graph that represents visitors who came with a school group?

(A) 325 degrees   (C) 180 degrees

(B) 243 degrees   (D) 117 degrees

MUSEUM VISITORS	
With a tour group	281
Visiting alone	97
With family	180
With a school group	325
With friend(s)	117

Circles, Graphs, and Angles (continued)

Support for Benchmarks MA.A.1.4.4. MA.A.3.4.3, MA.B.1.4.2, MA.E.1.4.1

2. Lucas needs to make a circle graph that represents data he has collected. The data are shown in the table.

Why will Lucas be unable to make a correct circle graph?

(F) The data do not add up to 100%.

(G) The data are not labeled correctly.

(H) The data are better suited to a line graph.

(I) The data need to be expressed in degrees.

Sedan	19%
Wagon	23%
Sport-utility vehicle	41%
Pick-up truck	11%

3. The table below shows how many customers at a cafeteria selected a particular entrée from Wednesday through Sunday.

ENTRÉE SELECTION

Fried chicken	1,575
Lasagna	756
Grilled salmon	882
Brisket	3,591
Roast turkey	1,008
Meatloaf	1,197
Pasta primavera	126
Baked cod	567
Honey-baked ham	1,606
Smothered pork chops	1,292
TOTAL CUSTOMERS	12,600

Part A Create a circle graph that shows the percent of customers that selected each entrée shown in the table.

Part B What were the two most popular entrées? What percent of customers selected one of these entrées?

Solving Linear Equations

Support for Benchmark MA.D.2.4.2

EXAMPLE 1 Solve the equation below for *x*.

$$-4x + 2x + 5 = 20 - 3x$$

$-2x + 5 = 20 - 3x$	Simplify by combining like terms.
$-2x + 5 + 3x = 20 - 3x + 3x$	Add $3x$ to both sides.
$x + 5 = 20$	
$x + 5 - 5 = 20 - 5$	Subtract 5 from both sides.
$x = 15$	

EXAMPLE 2 Kelly is knitting hats to sell at a carnival. It costs her $2 to make each hat, plus a one-time cost of $20 for knitting needles. If Kelly plans on selling the hats for $6 each, how many hats does she need to sell to break even?

Solution

In order to break even, the amount of money Kelly makes must equal the cost of making them.

$2h + 20 = 6h$	Write equation
$20 = 4h$	Subtract $2h$ from each side.
$5 = h$	Divide each side by 4.

Kelly must sell 5 hats to break even.

Exercises

1. Which of the following is the solution to the equation $\frac{-2 + x}{2} = 5$?

   (A) 27   (B) 12   (C) 10   (D) −20

2. What is the value of *n* in the equation below?
   $$\frac{4n}{3} + 3 = 3n - 2$$

3. What is the value of *x* in the equation below?
   $$5x - 20 = 16 + x$$

4. Solve for *x*: $14x - 72 = 8x$.

   (F) −8   (G) $3\frac{3}{11}$ (H) 12   (I) 15

5. Solve the equation below for *x*. Show your work.
   $$3x + 464 = 21x + 3x + 23$$

6. The sum of three numbers is 42. The second number is 5 less than half of the first number. The third number is 7 more than the first number. What are the three numbers? Show your work.

Distance and Midpoint Formulas

Support for Benchmark MA.C.3.4.2

EXAMPLES

Carlos wants to plant a tree halfway between his mailbox and the corner of his house. His mailbox is at $(-16, -28)$ on a map and the corner of his house is at $(-12, 0)$. Where should Carlos plant the tree? Use the midpoint formula.

$$M = \left(\frac{x_1 + x_2}{2}, \frac{y_1 + y_2}{2}\right)$$

$$M = \left(\frac{-16 + (-12)}{2}, \frac{-28 + 0}{2}\right)$$

$$M = \left(-\frac{28}{2}, -\frac{28}{2}\right)$$

$$M = (-14, -14)$$

Laura needs to find the distance between two artifacts on an archaeological site. The site is marked with a coordinate system. One artifact is located at $(-5, 3)$ and the other is located at $(8, -7)$. What is the distance between the two artifacts if each unit measures 2 feet? Use the distance formula.

$$D = \sqrt{(x_2 - x_1)^2 + (y_2 - y_1)^2}$$

$$D = \sqrt{(8 - (-5))^2 + (-7 - 3)^2}$$

$$D = \sqrt{(13)^2 + (-10)^2}$$

$$D = \sqrt{169 + 100}$$

$$D = \sqrt{269}$$

$$D \approx 16.40 \text{ units} = 32.80 \text{ feet}$$

Exercises

1. A survey states that a well marks the midpoint between a farmhouse and a large oak tree. On the survey map, the coordinates of the well are $(2, 3)$ and the coordinates of the farmhouse are $(-4, 8)$. What are the coordinates of the oak tree?

   (A) $(-2, 8)$ (B) $(-2, 11)$ (C) $\left(-1, 1\frac{1}{2}\right)$ (D) $(8, -2)$

2. Two ships are moving toward a rendezvous point. Ship A is 5 miles east and 4 miles north of the point. Ship B is 6 miles west and 1 mile north of the point. How many miles apart are the two ships? Round your answer to the nearest tenth of a mile.

3. Jaime needs to know the diagonal measurement of a storage unit on a blueprint. Opposite corners have the coordinates $(8, 7)$ and $(4, 4)$. What is the distance between the corners if 1 unit on the blueprint equals 1 meter?

   (F) 2.66 meters   (G) 4.23 meters   (H) 5 meters   (I) 7 meters

4. Segment AB lies on a coordinate grid. Its endpoints are at $(-1, 0)$ and $(7, 6)$.

   Part A What is the distance between point A and point B? Show your work.

   Part B If line CD bisects segment AB, what are the coordinates of the point at which it intersects the segment?

5. Austin stretched a rope across a lake. He anchored the rope at point $(-5, 8)$ and point $(-10, -4)$. What is the distance between the two anchors?

Use a Variety of Formulas

Support for Benchmarks MA.A.3.4.3, MA.B.1.4.1, MA.B.1.4.2, MA.B.2.4.2, MA.D.2.4.2

EXAMPLES

The fence around a rectangular yard measures 150 feet. The yard is 50 feet wide. How long is the yard?

$P = 2w + 2l$	Use the formula for perimeter.
$150 = 2(50) + 2l$	Substitute known values.
$150 = 100 + 2l$	
$50 = 2l$	
$l = 25$	

The yard is 25 feet long.

Casey ran $3\frac{1}{4}$ miles in 26 minutes. How many miles did Casey run per minute?

$d = rt$	Use the distance, rate, time formula.
$\frac{13}{4} = 26r$	Substitute known values. $3\frac{1}{4} = \frac{13}{4}$
$\frac{13}{4} \cdot \frac{1}{26} = r$	
$\frac{1}{8} = r$	

Casey ran $\frac{1}{8}$ mile per minute.

What is the area of a triangle with base 8 centimeters and height 6 centimeters?

$A = \frac{1}{2}bh$	Use the formula for area of a triangle.
$A = \frac{1}{2}(8)(6)$	Substitute.
$A = \frac{1}{2}(48)$	

$A = 24$ square centimeters

A circle has a circumference of 42π. What is the radius of the circle?

$C = 2\pi r$	Use the formula for circumference.
$42\pi = 2\pi r$	Substitute.
$42 = 2r$	
$21 = r$	

Exercises

1. Dana determined that her bathroom faucet was leaking 18 gallons of water in 4 hours. She called the plumber, who arrived 20 hours later. How much water leaked out of the faucet between Dana's phone call and the plumber's arrival? Use the formula $W = rt$ where W is the amount of water, r is the rate of leakage, and t is the time elapsed.

   (A) 108 gallons   (B) 90 gallons   (C) 45 gallons   (D) 4.4 gallons

2. The Hendersons drove from Key West to Atlanta, Georgia. They stopped in Jacksonville on their way to Atlanta.

   Part A Key West is 510 miles from Jacksonville. How long did it take the Hendersons to reach Jacksonville if they traveled at an average speed of 60 miles per hour? Show your work.

   Part B Jacksonville is about 350 miles from Atlanta. If the Hendersons were on the road a total of 6 hours from Jacksonville to Atlanta, what was their average speed from Jacksonville to Atlanta? Show your work.

3. A regular hexagon measures 10 inches on each side. What is the perimeter, in inches, of the hexagon?

Use a Variety of Formulas *(continued)*

Support for Benchmarks MA.A.3.4.3, MA.B.1.4.1, MA.B.1.4.2, MA.B.2.4.2, MA.D.2.4.2

4. Kirk can run $\frac{2}{10}$ of a mile in 1 minute. He runs an average of 4 hours per week. Using the formula $d = rt$, calculate the number of miles Kirk runs each week.

5. The garden shown is made up of semicircles and a square. Three semicircles border 3 sides of a square that measures 24 yards by 24 yards. The perimeter of the garden can be determined with the expression $3(\pi r) + s$ where r is the radius of the semicircle and s is the length of the side of the square.

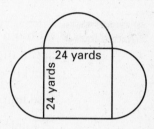

   Part A What is the perimeter of the garden? Use 3.14 for π.

   Part B What is the **total** area of the semicircular shaped parts of the garden?

6. A machine can put the wrappers on 5,000 granola bars per hour. The granola bars are shipped in cases containing 800 granola bars. How many **minutes** will it take the machine to put wrappers on enough granola bars for a case?

   Ⓕ 3.75 minutes   Ⓖ 5.8 minutes   Ⓗ 6.25 minutes   Ⓘ 9.6 minutes

7. A square has a perimeter of 24 units. A triangle has been drawn inside the square as shown. Which two formulas would you use to find the area of the triangle?

   Ⓐ $A = s^2$ and $A = \frac{1}{2} bh$ Ⓒ $P = 4s$ and $A = \frac{1}{2} bh$

   Ⓑ $A = s^2$ and $P = a + b + c$ Ⓓ $P = 4s$ and $P = a + b + c$

8. A tour bus traveled 252 miles in 6 hours. The 6 hours includes a $1\frac{1}{2}$ hour lunch break. What was the average speed, in miles per hour, of the bus while it was on the road?

9. Keysha rowed a boat on the Lazy River. She traveled 4 miles upstream (against the current) and then back downstream (with the current) the same distance, rowing at a constant speed. Keysha's trip upstream took 1 hour, and the trip downstream took 30 minutes. The river flows at a constant rate of 2 miles per hour.

   Part A Explain how the rate of the current affects Keysha's rates of traveling upstream and downstream.

   Part B Write an equation that you could use to find how quickly Keysha traveled when rowing upstream. Write another equation that you could use to find the speed at which Keysha traveled back downstream.

   Part C Solve one of your equations from Part A to determine Keysha's constant rowing speed in miles per hour.

Solve Measurement Problems

Support for Benchmarks MA.B.2.4.1, MA.B.2.4.2, MA.B.3.4.1

> You can use **unit analysis** to convert rated measures. **Estimation** is a skill you will need to solve real-world problems.

EXAMPLES

At room temperature, sound travels at a speed of about 771 miles per hour. How quickly does sound travel in feet per second?

Use unit analysis to convert.

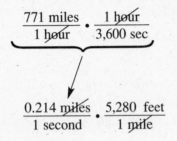

Multiply by hours per second to convert to seconds. Cancel units.

Multiply by feet per mile to convert to feet.

Sound travels at a rate of about 1,130 feet per second.

Annie bought a dozen apples. No one apple had a mass greater than 180 grams or less than 120 grams. ESTIMATE the total mass of all 12 apples in **kilograms.**

The maximum mass is
$180 \cdot 12 = 2,160$ g, or 2.16 kg.

The minimum mass is
$120 \cdot 12 = 1,440$ g, or 1.44 kg.

A reasonable estimate would fall between these measures.

The total mass is about 1.8 kilograms.

Exercises

1. Jenny is organizing her family reunion. She expects 200 people to attend, and she figures each person will eat two biscuits. It takes 250 grams of flour to make 10 biscuits. A bag of flour has a mass of 2.27 kilograms. How many bags of flour should Jenny buy to make enough biscuits for everyone at the family reunion?

   (A) 4 bags   (B) 5 bags   (C) 8 bags   (D) 10 bags

2. Peter is making leather key rings to give as holiday gifts this year. It takes Peter 20 minutes to make one key ring. How many **hours** will it take him to make 20 key rings?

   (F) $3\frac{2}{3}$ hours   (G) 6 hours   (H) $6\frac{2}{3}$ hours   (I) 9 hours

3. Paul Davis is a math teacher. It takes him between 5 and 10 minutes to grade a test. ESTIMATE the amount of time in **hours** it will take him to grade 24 tests.

4. Scientists believe that a Tyrannosaurus Rex could run no faster than 40 kilometers per hour. How many **meters per second** could a T-Rex run?

   (A) 40,000 m/sec   (B) 144 m/sec   (C) 66.7 m/sec   (D) 11.1 m/sec

Solve Measurement Problems *(continued)*

Support for Benchmarks MA.B.2.4.1, MA.B.2.4.2, MA.B.3.4.1

5. The employees at an advertising agency prefer an expensive brand of coffee. The office manager buys $\frac{1}{2}$ pound of this coffee every time the agency gets a new client. After 8 weeks, the office manager had bought 8 pounds of expensive coffee. What was the mean number of new clients the advertising agency got each week for those 8 weeks?

   (F) 8   (G) 4   (H) 2   (I) 1

6. Deon is driving from Miami to Seattle, Washington. He is making several stops along the 3,410-mile trip to visit friends and sightsee. On the first day, Deon travels 372 miles in 6 hours. On the second day, he travels 279 miles in $4\frac{1}{2}$ hours. He travels 651 miles in $10\frac{1}{2}$ hours on the third day. Assuming Deon continues to average the same speed, how many hours remain in his drive to Seattle after 3 days?

7. Rosa is filling a cardboard box with packing peanuts. She is using a dustpan to scoop the packing peanuts into the box. The shaded portion shows how full the box was after 3 scoops of packing peanuts.

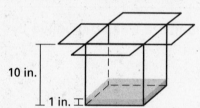

About how many **more** scoops of packing peanuts will Rosa need to add to the cardboard box to fill it to the top?

8. Jeff lives in the country. He wants to find out how far it is from his house to the main road. Jeff begins walking from his house. After 20 paces, he has covered the distance marked by the heavy line, shown below. Jeff knows that one of his paces covers about 30 inches.

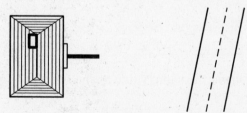

Part A About how many **feet** is it from Jeff's house to the main road?

Part B Use unit analysis to justify your answer.

Computing with Rational Numbers

Support for Benchmarks MA.A.2.4.2, MA.A.3.4.1. MA.A.3.4.2. MA.A.3.4.3

To arrive at the correct solution when computing with rational numbers, you will need to perform the operations in the correct order. Understanding the properties of numbers will also help you to arrive at the correct solution.

EXAMPLE 1 Evaluate the following expression.

$$\left(\frac{1}{3.5 - \frac{3}{2}}\right)^2 \cdot 22 - 2.5 = \left(\frac{1}{2}\right)^2 \cdot 22 - 2.5 \qquad \text{Evaluate parenthetical expressions.}$$
$$3.5 - \frac{3}{2} = 3.5 - 1.5 = 2$$
$$= \frac{1}{4} \cdot 22 - 2.5 \qquad \text{Evaluate exponential expressions.}$$
$$\left(\frac{1}{2}\right)^2 = \frac{1}{4}$$
$$= 5.5 - 2.5 \qquad \text{Multiply.}$$
$$\frac{1}{4} \cdot 22 = 5.5$$
$$= 3 \qquad \text{Subtract.}$$
$$5.5 - 2.5 = 3$$

EXAMPLE 2 Which of the following numbers when multiplied by $\left(\frac{1}{8}\right)^2$ is equal to 1?

(A) $-\left(\frac{1}{8}\right)^2$ (B) $\left(\frac{1}{-8}\right)^2$ (C) 8^2 (D) $-(8)^2$

Solution

$$\left(\frac{1}{8}\right)^2 = \frac{1}{64}$$

The reciprocal (multiplicative inverse) of $\frac{1}{64}$ is the only number that will

result in 1 when multiplied by $\frac{1}{64}$.

The reciprocal of $\frac{1}{64}$ is $\frac{64}{1}$ or 64.

64 can also be expressed as 8^2.

The answer is C, 8^2.

Exercises

1. Which expression does NOT have the same value as the others?

(A) $-\left(-\frac{1}{2}\right)^3$ (B) $\left(-\frac{1}{2}\right)^3$ (C) $\left(\frac{1}{2}\right)^3$ (D) $\frac{1}{2^3}$

2. Which of the following expressions can be simplified to 1?

(F) $(1{,}000 - 0.1)^1$ (G) $\left(\frac{1}{2}\right)^2$ (H) $\frac{\frac{1}{2}}{2}$ (I) $(x + 2)^0$

Computing with Rational Numbers
(continued)

Support for Benchmarks MA.A.2.4.2, MA.A.3.4.1. MA.A.3.4.2. MA.A.3.4.3

3. To evaluate the expression below, what should you do first?

$$(15 - 8)^2 - \left(3 - \frac{1}{3}\right)^2$$

   (A) Square 8 and square $\frac{1}{3}$.

   (B) Subtract 8, 3, and $\frac{1}{3}$ from 15.

   (C) Multiply -8 by 2 and $-\frac{1}{3}$ by 2.

   (D) Subtract 8 from 15 and $\frac{1}{3}$ from 3.

4. Clara could complete one of several operations first in the expression below and still arrive at the correct solution.

$$500 - [0.08(115) + 142 + 33] - 200$$

Which operation would lead Clara to an **incorrect** solution if she completed it FIRST?

   (F) Subtract 0.08 from 500.

   (G) Add 142 and 33.

   (H) Subtract 200 from 500.

   (I) Multiply 0.08 by 115.

5. What is the value of the expression below?

$$\left(\frac{1}{2}\right)^3 - \frac{5}{8} \cdot 4$$

   (A) -1 (B) -2 (C) $-\frac{19}{8}$ (D) $-\frac{21}{8}$

6. What is the value of the expression below?

$$(-1.2)^2 - 3.4^0$$

7. A jug of milk contains 1.89 liters. If about $\frac{1}{4}$ of the jug of milk is used for a recipe, ESTIMATE the number of liters of milk left in the jug.

8. Which is greater: $-5\frac{1}{2} + \left(-5\frac{1}{2}\right)$ or $-5 + \left(\frac{1}{2}\right) + (-5) + \left(\frac{1}{2}\right)$? Show your work to explain your answer.

9. When the multiplication is finished for the expression $\frac{7}{8} \times 6\frac{3}{4} \times 1 \times \left(-\frac{1}{3}\right)$, will the product be positive or negative? Explain.

10. A drop in barometric pressure suggests that rain or snow is likely. If the barometric pressure drops 0.6 inch in 4 hours, what is the average rate of change in pressure per hour?

FCAT Spiral Review

For use after Module 1

Solve for *x*.

1. $3x + 12 = 4 \cdot 18$

2. $32 + 5x = 128 - (3 \times 12)$

3. $15 + x = 3x - 9$

4. $25 + 2x = 7x - 30$

5. $8^2 + 6^2 = x^2$

6. $81 + x^2 = 225$

7. $3x + 24 = 4x - 28$

8. $16x - 72 = 12x + 16$

9. $4x + 48 = 24x - 40$

10. $7x + 84 = 10x - 30$

Find an equivalent measure to complete each statement.

11. 8 feet = _____ inches

12. 7 yards = _____ feet

13. 72 ounces = _____ pounds

14. 16 pints = _____ quarts

15. 2 hours 35 minutes = _____ minutes

16. 7 feet 7 inches = _____ inches

Find the value of *x*.

17.

Area = 81 square inches

18.

8 in.

x

Perimeter = 40 inches

19.

x

Circumference = 43.96 inches

Use the graph at the right for Exercises 20–23.

20. How many people were surveyed?

21. What percent of the people surveyed chose vanilla, to the nearest percent?

22. What fraction of the people surveyed chose chocolate?

23. Suppose that 270 people had been surveyed instead of 108. If the relative sizes of the graph sectors stayed the same, how many people out of 270 would have chosen vanilla?

24. Find the coordinates of the midpoint of the segment that connects the points $(-6, -4)$ and $(-8, 10)$.

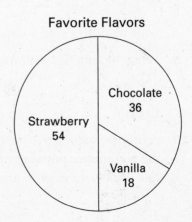

Favorite Flavors

Chocolate 36

Strawberry 54

Vanilla 18

Name _____ Date _____

Range and Measures of Central Tendency

Support for Benchmark MA.E.1.4.2

EXAMPLE 1 The times for the first five runners in a marathon are listed below.

4 h 4 min
4 h 38 min
4 h 52 min
5 h 3 min
5 h 15 min

What is the mean time, **in minutes**, of the first five runners?

Solution

To find the mean, add the data together and divide by the number of items of data.

Convert the times to minutes. Then add.

$244 + 278 + 292 + 303 + 315 = 1{,}432$

Divide the total by 5, for the number of items of data.

$1{,}432 \div 5 = 286.4$ minutes.

EXAMPLE 2 The sales for Jane, a furniture salesperson, are listed below.

$599, $899, $219, $99, $599, $399, $249, $359

What is the range of the data? Which measure of central tendency would make Jane's sales seem as high as possible: mean, median, or mode?

Solution

The range of the data is the difference between the greatest and least data items: $899 − $99 = $800.

Estimate the mean for Jane's sales: $600 + 900 + 200 + 100 + 600 + 400 + 200 + 400 = 3{,}400$. $3,400 \div 8$ is roughly $400 dollars.

The median is the data item that falls in the middle of the set. Arranged in order, the data are $99, $219, $249, $359, $399, $599, $599, $899. The middle item would fall halfway between $359 and $399, or about $380.

The mode is the data item that appears most often. $599 appears twice.

The mode is the measure that makes Jane's sales seem the highest.

Exercises

1. What is the median for the data listed below?

312   427   289   368   709   426   405   389   291   516

2. Dedrick recorded the price of his newest stock every week for 12 weeks.

$91\frac{1}{4}$ $90\frac{1}{2}$ 90 $90\frac{1}{4}$ $91\frac{1}{4}$ $91\frac{1}{2}$

$90\frac{3}{4}$ 91 $90\frac{1}{2}$ $90\frac{1}{4}$ $89\frac{3}{4}$ $90\frac{1}{2}$

What is the mode for this set of data?

(A) $90\frac{1}{2}$ (B) $90\frac{5}{8}$ (C) $91\frac{1}{4}$ (D) $91\frac{3}{8}$

Range and Measures of Central Tendency
(continued) Support for Benchmark MA.E.1.4.2

3. Kevin recorded the high temperature and general weather conditions in Orlando every day for a week.

   94 (sunny), 91 (mostly cloudy), 88 (cloudy), 81 (raining), 88 (partly cloudy), 96 (mostly sunny), 89 (partly cloudy)

   After examining the data, Kevin made this statement about the data: *If the temperature is above 90 degrees, then it is mostly sunny or sunny.*

   Which of the following is NOT true of Kevin's statement?

   (F) The statement is false.

   (G) The inverse of the statement is true.

   (H) The converse of the statement is true.

   (I) The contrapositive of the statement is true.

4. Professor Reedy gave her freshman physics class a quiz. The scores are listed below.

   12   88   92   78   34   76   12   90   82   94

   Which of these measures would BEST represent most students' performance on the quiz?

   (A) mode   (B) median   (C) mean   (D) range

5. The high temperatures for Hotsville are listed below.

July 1	July 2	July 3	July 4	July 5	July 6	July 7
93	96	94	95	82	82	92

   Which measure makes the temperature in Hotsville seem the most comfortable to a person who prefers temperatures in the 80s?

   (F) mode   (G) median   (H) mean   (I) range

6. The Kwans are looking for a house in the Forest Hills neighborhood. Their real estate agent gives them a list of the houses in the neighborhood that were sold most recently and their selling price.

   $88,000 $120,000 $112,000 $120,000

   Which of these measures would give an observer the clearest picture of home prices in Forest Hills?

   (A) mode   (B) median   (C) mean   (D) range

7. What is the range of the data below?

   198, 205, 611, 315, 567, 302, 198, 420, 376, 250, 421, 392

8. What is the mean of the data below?

   6.9, 5.7, 6.1, 7.0, 5.8, 6.2, 7.8, 5.5

Interpreting Graphs

Support for Benchmarks MA.E.1.4.1, MA.E.3.4.1

EXAMPLE 1 In the box-and-whisker plot, what is median of the set of data?

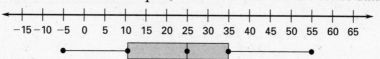

Remember, a box-and-whisker plot clearly shows the median and upper and lower quartiles of a set of data. The median is marked by a line through the box. The upper and lower quartiles form the sides of the box. The "whiskers" show the highest and lowest values for the data set. For the box-and-whisker plot shown, the median is 25.

EXAMPLE 2 Amy tracked the per-pound price of chicken breasts at two different grocery stores over 10 weeks. A line graph of her data is shown.

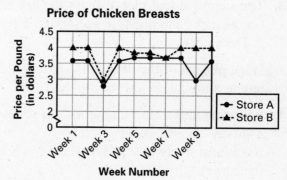

During which week did the two grocery stores sell chicken breasts for the same price per pound?

(A) Week 1   (C) Week 7

(B) Week 3   (D) Week 9

If chicken breasts were the same price, then the lines on the graph would meet. The only point at which the lines meet is Week 7. The answer is C.

EXAMPLE 3 The stem-and-leaf plot shows the heights, in inches, of the varsity cheerleaders at Hoover High.

```
5 | 9
6 | 1 2 2 4 6 7 9
7 | 1 2          Key: 6|2 = 62
```

What percent of the cheerleaders are less than 5 feet 5 inches tall?

Solution

Change 5 feet 5 inches to inches.
5 feet 5 inches = 5 · (12 inches) + 5 inches = 65 inches.

Count the number of data items on the **right** side of the vertical line that are less than 65 inches. There are 5 cheerleaders less than 65 inches tall.

Five out of 10 total cheerleaders is 50%.

Exercises

1. Josie collected the following data: 12, 15, 14, 18, 10, 19, and 12. She displayed the data in the stem-and-leaf plot shown below.

   ```
   1 | 0 2 4 5 8 9
   ```

   What mistake did Josie make in her stem-and-leaf plot?

Interpreting Graphs *(continued)*

Support for Benchmarks MA.E.1.4.1, MA.E.3.4.1

2. The graph at the right shows the Guzmans' total utility bill (electricity and water) and just their electric bill.

What was the highest **water bill** the Guzmans received?

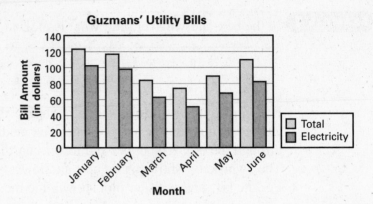

Guzmans' Utility Bills

3. The stem-and-leaf plot displays the low temperatures (in degrees Fahrenheit) in Jacksonville for two weeks in December.

What percent of the days in December did the temperature fall below 40 degrees?

```
3 | 4 6 7 9
4 | 1 2 3 3 6 6
5 | 0 2 4 5        Key: 4|2 = 42
```

4. Four candidates are running for governor. A news station conducted a survey each week for 4 weeks asking people which candidate they were most likely to vote for. The table below shows the results of the survey.

Governor's Race Survey Results

Date	Candidate A	Candidate B	Candidate C	Candidate D
9 Oct	245	198	55	2
16 Oct	268	201	31	0
23 Oct	212	248	38	2
30 Oct	198	271	30	1
Totals	923	918	154	5

The election is on November 6. Which candidate is most likely to win the election?

(A) Candidate A   (B) Candidate B   (C) Candidate C   (D) Candidate D

5. What is the median for the box-and-whisker plot shown?

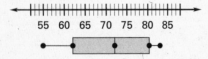

Interpreting Graphs *(continued)*

Support for Benchmarks MA.E.1.4.1, MA.E.3.4.1

6. The box-and-whisker plot displays the number of points scored by the football team during each game.

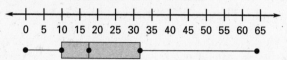

Sam looks at the box-and-whisker plot and incorrectly concludes that half the team's scores were over 32 points. Write a statement that corrects Sam's misinterpretation.

7. Five different book clubs meet in a bookstore. The store manager asked members of each club which type of book they preferred to read for pleasure. The manager's survey results are listed by book club below.

Bookstore Manager's Survey Results

Club Name	Fiction/ Literature	Nonfiction	Sci fi/ Fantasy	Mystery	Romance
Seven Sisters	2		1	2	2
Mystery Meet	1	1		8	
Coffee Klatch	3				1
Bluestockings	5	2		1	
Readers	6	1	3		
Totals	**17**	**4**	**4**	**11**	**3**

Which of the following statements can be verified?

Ⓕ Most of the people who chose science fiction/fantasy are men.

Ⓖ More people chose fiction/literature than mystery and nonfiction combined.

Ⓗ Over half of the members of the Seven Sisters book club chose mystery as their favorite genre.

Ⓘ Members of the Coffee Klatch book club were too busy drinking coffee to participate in the survey.

8. The table shows the population of Hernando County, Florida, over 50 years.

YEAR	POPULATION
1950	6,693
1960	11,205
1970	17,004
1980	44,469
1990	101,115
2000	130,802

Part A Make a line graph of the population of Hernando County for the years shown in the table.

Part B During the twentieth century, Hernando County became a popular place to retire. Between which two consecutive census years did Hernando County become a haven for retirees? Explain.

Part C Predict the population of Hernando County for the year 2010. Explain how you determined your answer.

Using Properties to Simplify Expressions

Support for Benchmarks MA.A.2.4.2, MA.A.3.4.2, MA.A.3.4.3

EXAMPLE 1 In the formula $P = \frac{1}{3}(5t - v)$, P is a band member's pay, v and is the band's travel expenses, and t is the number of tickets sold. The band spends $90 traveling to a concert venue. They sell 204 tickets. How much is each band member paid?

$$P = \frac{1}{3}(5t - v)$$ Write the formula.

$$= \frac{1}{3}[5(204) - 90]$$ Substitute values for variables.

$$= 5(68) - 30$$ Distribute the $\frac{1}{3}$.

$$= 310$$ Simplify.

Each band member is paid $310.

EXAMPLE 2 Simplify the expression below.
$3(2x + 2y) - 8(x + y) + 2(y - 2x)$
Multiply through to clear parentheses and then combine like terms.

$6x + 6y - 8x - 8y + 2y - 4x$ Use the fact that $a(b + c) = ab + ac$.

$(6x - 8x - 4x) + (6y - 8y + 2y)$ Group like terms.

$\quad -6x \qquad + \qquad 0$ Simplify.

The expression can be simplified to $-6x$.

Exercises

Simplify the expressions.

1. $(2x + 3) + (4 + x)$

2. $3(5 - x) - 4(x + 2)$

3. $(8 - 3 - 5)(x + 4 + y)$

4. $15.5\left(\dfrac{x}{6.2 - 1.2}\right)$

5. Irene hires woodworkers to make deck chairs for her outdoor furniture company. The materials for a single chair cost Irene $40, and she pays each woodworker $20 per hour (t). She charges customers $160 for each deck chair. The formula below shows Irene's profit (P) for the number of chairs built (c).

$P = c(160 - 40 - 20t)$

A woodworker builds 4 deck chairs, and each chair takes 2 hours to build. What is Irene's profit for these deck chairs?

6. If evaluated, which of the following expressions simplifies to 1?

(A) $\dfrac{2}{2x + 4}(3x - 4 - 2x + 6)$

(C) $\dfrac{1}{2}(6y - 4x)$

(B) $\dfrac{3}{x(4x - 2 - 3x - 1)}$

(D) $3(x + y) - 3(x - y) + y(11 - 5)$

Solving and Using Linear Equations

Support for Benchmark MA.D.2.4.2

EXAMPLE What is the value of x in the following equation?

$6(x + 6) - 4x = 3x + 18 + 5x$	Equation
$6x + 36 - 4x = 3x + 18 + 5x$	Use distributive property.
$2x + 36 = 8x + 18$	Combine like terms.
$36 = 6x + 18$	Subtract $2x$ from each side.
$18 = 6x$	Subtract 18 from each side.
$3 = x$	Divide each side by 6.

Exercises

1. What is the value of x in the following equation?
$3(x - 12) + 3x = 324$

(A) 48   (B) 56   (C) 60   (D) 63

2. The equation $O = p - 0.07i$ is used to determine whether Oscar owes income tax to the state or the state owes Oscar a refund. The variable p represents how much Oscar has already paid the state, and i represents his taxable income. This year Oscar paid the state $1,826 and his taxable income was $24,600. Determine whether Oscar owes income tax to the state or the state owes Oscar a refund, and calculate how much money is owed.

3. What is the value for x in the following equation?
$$\frac{x + 6}{2} = \frac{39 - x}{3}$$

(F) −8   (G) 6   (H) 12   (I) 30

4. What is the value of x in the following equation?
$$\frac{x + 2x - 6}{3} = 8$$

(A) 10   (B) 12   (C) 14   (D) 38

5. The Johnsons spent the weekend at the beach. The equation $E = 180h + (f + s)$ represents their expenses, where h is the number of nights at the hotel, f is the amount spent on food, and s is the amount spent on souvenirs. The Johnsons stayed 2 nights at the hotel and spent $174 on food and $41 on souvenirs. What were the Johnsons' expenses for their weekend at the beach? Show your work.

Comparing and Ordering Numbers

Support for Benchmarks MA.A.1.4.2, MA.A.1.4.3, MA.A.1.4.4

EXAMPLE 1 Which of the following numbers is closest to $\frac{1}{25}$?

(A) $\frac{441}{10,000}$ (B) $\frac{8}{100}$ (C) $\sqrt{0.125}$ (D) 0.004

$\frac{1}{25} = 0.04$ Determine the decimal value of $\frac{1}{25}$ to make it easier to compare to the answer choices.

Determine the decimal value of all the answer choices.

$\frac{441}{10,000} = 0.0441$ $\frac{8}{100} = 0.08$

$\sqrt{0.125} \approx 0.3536$ 0.004

The answer is A. Choices B and C are much greater than $\frac{1}{25}$ and choice D is much smaller.

EXAMPLE 2 Points W, X, Y, and Z are shown on the number line.

Which of the following numbers falls between X and Y on the number line?

(A) -2.75 (B) 0   (C) $\frac{4}{5}$ (D) $\sqrt{2}$

Point X falls on -2.25 and point Y falls on 0.25. $\frac{4}{5}$ and $\sqrt{2}$ are both greater than 0.25, and -2.75 is less than -2.25. The correct answer is B, 0.

Exercises

1. Which list is in order from **least** to **greatest**?

   (A) $3\sqrt{7}$, $2\sqrt{17}$, 8.03, $\frac{493}{62}$ (C) $3\sqrt{7}$, $\frac{493}{62}$, 8.03, $2\sqrt{17}$

   (B) $\frac{493}{62}$, $2\sqrt{17}$, $3\sqrt{7}$, 8.03 (D) $2\sqrt{17}$, 8.03, $\frac{493}{62}$, $3\sqrt{7}$

2. Given the inequalities below, what could be the value of x?

   $\frac{1}{x} > 0.03$ $\frac{1}{x} < \sqrt{0.01}$

   (F) 50   (G) 25   (H) $\sqrt{25}$ (I) -4

3. Stela has been monitoring the weather. This spring, it has rained $\frac{45}{50}$ days. What is this number expressed as a decimal?

4. Points K, L, M, and N are on the number line.

   Which point falls between $-\sqrt{9}$ and $-\frac{8}{3}$?

   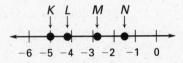

   (A) Point K (C) Point M

   (B) Point L (D) Point N

5. A statistic is expressed as 0.244. Which fraction is equivalent?

   (F) $\frac{122}{5,000}$ (G) $\frac{61}{250}$ (H) $\frac{31}{125}$ (I) $\frac{244}{100}$

Angle Pair Relationships

Support for Benchmark MA.C.2.4.1

EXAMPLE When put together, the pieces of stained glass shown will form part of a circle.

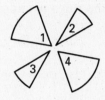

When fit together, piece 1 and piece 2 form a right angle. Piece 2 and piece 4 also form a right angle. If piece 1 has an angle measure of 60 degrees, what is the angle measure, in degrees, of piece 4?

Solution

$m\angle 1 + m\angle 2 = 90°$
$m\angle 4 + m\angle 2 = 90°$

So, $m\angle 1 + m\angle 2 = m\angle 4 + m\angle 2$ and $m\angle 1 = m\angle 4$.

It is given that $m\angle 1 = 60°$. Therefore $m\angle 1 = m\angle 4 = 60°$.

Exercises

1. Dustin divided his bulletin board into four areas, as shown at the right.

   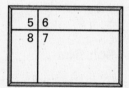

   Dustin determined that angle 6 measures 90 degrees. Which of the following is NOT true of the angles Dustin created on his bulletin board?

   (A) All the angles are congruent.

   (B) All the angles are right angles.

   (C) Angles 7 and 8 are vertical angles.

   (D) Angles 6 and 7 are a linear pair.

2. Kevin used a rod to stake up a plant. Initially the rod formed a right angle with the ground, but after a while the rod began to lean toward the plant. Kevin determines that on the side toward the plant, the rod is making an angle with the ground that measures roughly 20 degrees less than the measure of the adjacent angle. What is the approximate measure of the **adjacent** angle?

3. On the street map below, Main Street intersects Pine Street.

   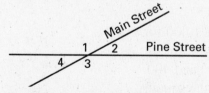

   Which of the following describes the angle pair formed by the angles designated 1 and 2?

   (F) complementary   (G) congruent   (H) vertical angles   (I) linear pair

Operations with Exponents

Support for Benchmarks MA.A.1.4.4, MA.A.3.4.1, MA.A.3.4.2, MA.A.3.4.3

Recall the rules to simplify expressions with exponents.

$$x^2 \cdot x^3 = x^{2+3} = x^5 \qquad \frac{x^{12}}{x^4} = x^{12-4} = x^8 \qquad (x^3)^2 = x^{3 \cdot 2} = x^6$$

The rules also hold true for negative exponents. Recall that a negative exponent indicates an inverse. For example, 2^{-2} means $\frac{1}{2^2}$ or $\frac{1}{4}$.

A negative exponent in the denominator of a fraction can be made positive and moved to the numerator. For example, $\frac{3}{x^{-3}}$ is equivalent to $3x^3$.

EXAMPLE 1 Which of the following BEST simplifies the expression below?

$$\frac{2x^2y(x^2 + 4y^3 + 8)}{xy}$$

(A) $2x^3 + 8xy^3 + 16x$

(C) $x^3 + 4xy^3 + 4x$

(B) $2x^3 + 8xy^2 + 16x$

(D) $2x^3 + 6xy^2 + 10x$

Solution

$\dfrac{xy \cdot 2x(x^2 + 4y^3 + 8)}{xy}$ Note the common factor in the numerator and denominator, xy.

$2x(x^2 + 4y^3 + 8)$ Simplify. $\dfrac{xy}{xy} = 1$

$2x \cdot x^2 + 2x \cdot 4y^3 + 2x \cdot 8$ Distribute.

$2x^3 + 8xy^3 + 16x$ Evaluate. $2x \cdot x^2 = 2x^1 \cdot x^2 = 2x^3$

EXAMPLE 2 Lyle is using the equation below to find the diagonal measurement of a city block.

$$c^2 = a^2 + b^2$$

Lyle knows a equals 1,000 feet and b equals a plus 400 feet. What is the diagonal measurement of the city block?

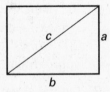

Solution

$c^2 = (1,000)^2 + (1,000 + 400)^2$ Substitute 1,000 for a and 1,000 + 400 for b.

$c^2 = (1,000)^2 + (1,400)^2$ Add 1,000 and 400.

$c^2 = 1,000,000 + 1,960,000$ Simplify the squares.

$c^2 = 2,960,000$ Add.

$c \approx 1,720.5$ feet   Calculate the square root.

Exercises

1. Simplify the expression $6x^2y(x^{-2}y^3 + 5)$, when $x = 3$ and $y = 2$.

Operations with Exponents *(continued)*

Support for Benchmarks MA.A.1.4.4, MA.A.3.4.1, MA.A.3.4.2, MA.A.3.4.3

2. Which of the following BEST simplifies the expression $\dfrac{xy(5x)^2}{y^{-3}}$?

(A) $\dfrac{5x^3}{y^{-2}}$ (B) $\dfrac{5x^2}{y^{-2}}$ (C) $25x^2y^3$ (D) $25x^3y^4$

3. Which of the following numbers when multiplied by 5^{-3} is equal to 1?

(F) 3^{-5} (G) 5^3 (H) $\left(\dfrac{1}{5}\right)^3$ (I) -5^3

4. Which of the following is NOT equivalent to the expression $\dfrac{3x^{-2}y^2z}{x^2yz^{-3}}$?

(A) $\dfrac{3 \cdot y \cdot z \cdot z \cdot z \cdot z}{x \cdot x \cdot x \cdot x}$ (C) $\dfrac{3y^{2+1}z^1 \cdot 3}{x^{2 \cdot 2}}$

(B) $\dfrac{3y^{2-1}z^{1+3}}{x^{2+2}}$ (D) $\dfrac{3y^2z \cdot z^3}{x^2y \cdot x^2}$

5. The Keyes want to know how much they will have in a savings account after 10 years. The account earns interest at an annual rate that is compounded monthly. The Keyes can use the formula below to calculate the value of their savings account.

$$A = p\left(1 + \dfrac{0.05}{n}\right)^{nt}$$

In this formula, A is the amount after t years at an interest rate of 0.05 compounded n times per year if the starting amount was p. The Keyes put $5,000 in the account initially. How much will be in the account after 10 years, assuming there are no withdrawals or fees?

6. Emily is using the formula below to calculate the combined volume, in cubic centimeters, of two objects.
$$V = s^3 + b^2h$$
If $s = 8$, $b = (h - 2)$, and $h = 10$, what is V in cubic centimeters?

7. What is the value of the expression $12(2)^{-2}(3)^3$?

(F) 1,296   (G) 162   (H) 81   (I) 27

8. M, N, O, and P are four points on the number line at the right.
Which point represents a number that, when cubed, will result in a number greater than itself?

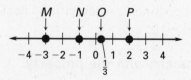

(A) Point M (B) Point N (C) Point O (D) Point P

9. Which of the following is equivalent to the expression $\dfrac{3x^2y^{-3}}{2z^{-2}}$?

(F) $\dfrac{3x^2z^2}{2y^3}$ (G) $\dfrac{3}{2}(x^2y^3z^2)$ (H) $(1.5xyz)^3$ (I) $1.5x^2\left(\dfrac{1}{y^3}\right)$

FCAT Spiral Review

For use after Module 2

Simplify each expression.

1. $7x + 3x^2 + 4x + 15$

2. $12x + 3y - 8x + 6y$

3. $4x^2 - 3y^3 + 7x - 2x^2 - 3x$

4. $4(3x - 5) - x(y + 4x + 5)$

5. $6x(2x^2 - 9) - y(y^2 + 2x + 7)$

6. $12 - 5(x + y) + y(x + y - 8)$

Write <, >, or = in the blank.

7. 87 ____ 78

8. $\dfrac{2}{4}$ ____ $\dfrac{3}{8}$

9. 0.094 ____ 0.804

10. 4^3 ____ 8^2

11. $\dfrac{7}{8}$ ____ 0.78

12. 3^4 ____ 5^3

Write the numbers from least to greatest.

13. $3, 8, 4, 11, 17$

14. $410, 170, 401, 107, 701$

15. $0.8, 0.08, 8.0, 0.808, 0.008$

16. $\dfrac{1}{3}, \dfrac{2}{4}, \dfrac{2}{7}, \dfrac{8}{9}, \dfrac{4}{5}$

17. $3^4, 4^3, 7^2, 2^5, 5^3$

18. $\dfrac{1}{8}, 0.4, \dfrac{3}{12}, 0.53, \dfrac{5}{9}$

The histogram shows the numbers of times Maya went to the park during a period of 12 weeks last year.

19. How many times did Maya go to the park during weeks 10–12?

20. Can you determine the number of times that Maya went to the park during week 8? Explain.

21. Can you predict the number of times that Maya went to the park during weeks 13–15 last year? Explain why or why not.

Maya's Trips to the Park

22. If the pattern continues, what will the next number be?
$-1, -3, -6, -10, -15, \ldots$

Match the statement with the property.

23. If $m\angle B = 20°$, then $2(m\angle B) = 40°$.

A. Reflexive property of equality

24. If $DE = EF$ and $EF = FG$, then $DE = FG$.

B. Transitive property of equality

25. For any angle C, $m\angle C = m\angle C$.

C. Multiplication property of equality

26. If $m\angle A = m\angle B$, then $m\angle B = m\angle A$.

D. Symmetric property of equality

27. On a number line, $\sqrt{54}$ would fall between which two integers?

Powers of 10 and Scientific Notation

Support for Benchmarks MA.A.1.4.2, MA.A.1.4.3, MA.A.1.4.4, MA.A.3.4.1

To express a number in **scientific notation**, place a decimal after the first non-zero digit. Then count the number of places from the new decimal to the original decimal. That number will be the power of 10 in scientific notation. If you count to the right, the power will be positive; if you count to the left, the power will be negative.

EXAMPLE The mean distance from Earth to the Sun is 93,000,000 miles. Express this number in scientific notation.

9.3000000   Place the new decimal after the first nonzero digit. There are 7 places between the new decimal and the old decimal.

9.3×10^7 miles   Write the number in scientific notation.

Exercises

1. Which of the following lists the numbers in order from **least** to **greatest**?

    (A) 5.4×10^{-3}, 0.025^2, $\frac{1}{500}$, $\sqrt{0.0169}$

    (B) 0.025^2, $\frac{1}{500}$, 5.4×10^{-3}, $\sqrt{0.0169}$

    (C) $\sqrt{0.0169}$, 0.025^2, $\frac{1}{500}$, 5.4×10^{-3}

    (D) $\frac{1}{500}$, 5.4×10^{-3}, $\sqrt{0.0169}$, 0.025^2

2. Which of the following has the **greatest** value?

    (F) 9.8×10^{17} (G) 2.1×10^{-10} (H) 1.4×10^{-1} (I) 4.56×10^{-2}

3. Tyrell knows that Earth is about 1.5×10^8 kilometers from the Sun. Saturn is about 10 times as far from the Sun as Earth. Which of the following BEST describes what happens when 1.5×10^8 kilometers is multiplied by 10 and the result is written in scientific notation?

    (A) The power of 10 will decrease by 1.

    (B) The power of 10 will stay the same, and the decimal will move to the left.

    (C) The power of 10 will stay the same, and the decimal will move to the right.

    (D) The power of 10 will increase by 1.

4. What is the value of the expression $3.4 \times 10^4 + 6.2 \times 10^3$? Express your answer in standard notation.

Angle Pair Relationships and Perpendicular Lines

Support for Benchmark MA.C.1.4.1

EXAMPLE In the figure, ∠ABC and ∠CBD are congruent.

What is the measure of ∠CBD?

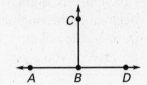

Solution

If two lines intersect to form a linear pair of congruent angles, then the lines are perpendicular.

Therefore, $m\angle CBD = 90°$.

Exercises

1. The side of a doorframe makes a right angle with the floor. Which of the following BEST describes the relationship between the side of the doorframe and the floor?

   Ⓕ The side of the doorframe is parallel to the floor.

   Ⓖ The side of the doorframe is perpendicular to the floor.

   Ⓗ The side of the doorframe and the floor form alternate interior angles.

   Ⓘ The side of the doorframe and the floor form complementary angles.

2. Determine the value of x, in degrees, in the figure shown.

   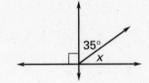

3. What is the measure of ∠KLM?

   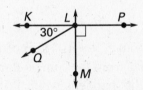

   Ⓐ 30 degrees   Ⓑ 60 degrees   Ⓒ 90 degrees   Ⓓ 180 degrees

4. In the figure, $\overleftrightarrow{CF}$ is perpendicular to $\overleftrightarrow{AE}$. The measure of angle ∠BDA is 60°, and ∠EDG and ∠HGI are congruent.

   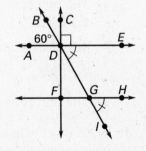

   What is the measure of ∠DGF? Show your work. Explain in words, or provide a proof showing how to find the measure of ∠DGF.

Parallel Lines and Transversals

Support for Benchmark MA.C.1.4.1

EXAMPLE   On the street map, Main Street and Elm Street
are parallel. Building A is on a corner that
measures 62°. What is the measure, in degrees,
of the corner where Building C is located?

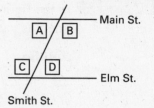

Solution

In the diagram, angles A and C are consecutive
interior angles.

$$m\angle A + m\angle C = 180°$$
$$62° + m\angle C = 180°$$
$$m\angle C = 118°$$

The measure of the corner where Building C is located
is 118°.

Exercises

1. In the figure shown, $\overleftrightarrow{AB}$ is parallel to $\overleftrightarrow{CD}$.

   Which of the following statements is true?

   (A) $m\angle AFE + m\angle EFB = 180°$ (B) $\angle EFB \cong \angle CGF$

   (C) $m\angle CGH + m\angle FGD = 180°$ (D) $\angle AFE \cong \angle CGH$

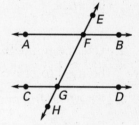

2. Two parallel lines are cut by a transversal. Angles A and B
   are consecutive interior angles in this intersection. Angle A
   has a measure of 55°. What is the measure, in degrees, of $\angle B$?

3. In the figure shown, line m is parallel to line n.

   What is the value of x?

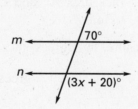

4. In the figure shown, $\overleftrightarrow{MP}$ is parallel to $\overleftrightarrow{LQ}$ and $\overleftrightarrow{NQ}$ is
   perpendicular to $\overleftrightarrow{KO}$. The measure of $\angle LRK$ is 35°.

   What is the measure, in degrees, of $\angle NPM$? Show your
   work. Explain in words, or provide a proof showing
   how to find the measure of $\angle NPM$.

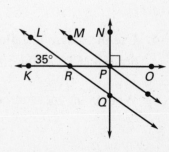

Properties of Parallel Lines

Support for Benchmarks MA.C.1.4.1, MA.C.2.4.1

EXAMPLE In the figure, $m\angle 1 = m\angle 2 = m\angle 4$. Show that line p is parallel to line r.

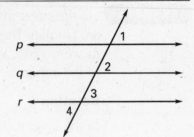

Solution

$\angle 1$ and $\angle 2$ are corresponding angles. If $m\angle 1 = m\angle 2$, then line p is parallel to line q. $\angle 3$ and $\angle 4$ are vertical angles, so $m\angle 3 = m\angle 4$. Using substitution, it follows that $m\angle 3 = m\angle 2$.

Because $\angle 2$ and $\angle 3$ are corresponding angles, line q is parallel to line r. Therefore line p is parallel to line r.

Exercises

1. In the figure at the right, $\angle 1$ and $\angle 2$ are corresponding angles.

   Which of the following cases would be sufficient to prove that line a and line b are parallel?

   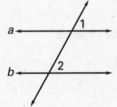

   (A) $\angle 1 \cong \angle 2$ (B) line $a \perp$ line b

   (C) $m\angle 1 + m\angle 2 = 180°$ (D) $2(m\angle 1) = 180°$

2. Use the figure at the right. Which of the following CANNOT be used to prove that $\overleftrightarrow{AB}$ is parallel to $\overleftrightarrow{CD}$?

   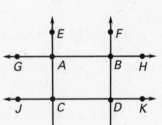

   (F) $\overleftrightarrow{AB} \perp \overleftrightarrow{BD}$ and $\overleftrightarrow{CD} \perp \overleftrightarrow{BD}$

   (G) $m\angle CAB + m\angle ACD = 180°$

   (H) $m\angle CAB + m\angle ABD = 180°$

   (I) $m\angle EAB = m\angle JCL$

3. In the figure, $\angle 1$ measures 90° and $\angle 4$ measures 130°. Line c is parallel to line d.

   What is the measure, in degrees, of $\angle 7$?

   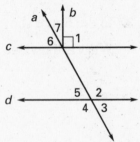

4. Use the diagram. Jaime is building a cedar chest. The top $(\overline{AB})$ and bottom $(\overline{CD})$ of the chest are parallel.

   What is the measure, in degrees, of $\angle BCD$?

   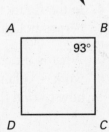

Linear Relationships

Support for Benchmarks MA.B.2.4.2, MA.C.3.4.2, MA.D.1.4.2, MA.D.2.4.2

EXAMPLE 1 An Internet Web site gets 200 visits per day. How many visits does it get in a 30-day month?

Solution

Use unit analysis: $\dfrac{200 \text{ visits}}{1 \text{ day}} \cdot \dfrac{30 \text{ days}}{1 \text{ month}} = \dfrac{6{,}000 \text{ visits}}{1 \text{ month}}$

6,000 visits will occur in a 30-day month.

EXAMPLE 2 Trey types at a rate of 60 words per minute. Write an equation to represent the number of words Trey can type in a certain time frame.

Solution

The equation of a line in slope-intercept form is $y = mx + b$. If you graphed Trey's typing speed, the speed would be the slope, or m. The number of words Trey can type would be y and the number of minutes would be x. In this case, $b = 0$ because at 0 minutes Trey has typed 0 words.

The equation is $y = 60x$.

EXAMPLE 3 The graph for the cost of a cab ride to the airport is shown at the right.

The slope of the line is $\dfrac{85}{100}$. What does the slope represent?

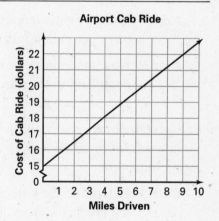

Solution

The slope of a line is the change in y divided by the change in x. In this case, y is the cost of the cab ride and x is the number of miles. Therefore, slope represents the cost of the cab ride per mile.

Exercises

1. Natasha walks on the treadmill for 20 minutes 5 times per week. She walks at a constant rate of 3 miles per hour. How many miles does Natasha walk, per week, on the treadmill?

Linear Relationships *(continued)*

Support for Benchmarks MA.B.2.4.2, MA.C.3.4.2, MA.D.1.4.2, MA.D.2.4.2

2. The following system of equations represents the yearly earnings of Employee A and Employee B. In both equations, the *y*-intercept represents the employees' annual bonus. Employee A earns $20 per hour, and Employee B earns $22.50 per hour.

$$A = 20x + 750$$
$$B = 22.5x + 1{,}000$$

If the two employees worked the same number of hours last year and Employee A's yearly earnings were $40,910, how much were Employee B's yearly earnings?

  Ⓐ $47,867.50   Ⓑ $46,180   Ⓒ $45,180   Ⓓ $41,160

3. Sabrina has completed 120 miles of a 400-mile road trip. Today she plans to travel for 4 hours at an average speed of 60 miles per hour. The equation $y = 60x + 120$ represents how many miles of her trip Sabrina will have completed after today's drive.

What will be the value of *y*, in miles, if Sabrina follows her plan for the day's drive?

4. The equation $C = 1.2g$ represents the cost of gasoline, where *g* is the number of gallons and *C* is the total cost.

  Part A Write an equation representing the cost of gasoline if the price per gallon rose to $1.50.

  Part B How much **more** would 10 gallons of gasoline cost, compared to the previous price, if the cost of gasoline rose to $1.50 per gallon?

5. Cable Internet service for businesses costs a certain amount for installation plus a monthly fee, as shown on the graph.

  Part A Determine the *y*-intercept of a line joining the points on the graph. Explain what the *y*-intercept represents.

  Part B Determine the slope of the line.

  Part C Explain what the slope represents.

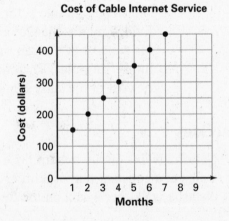

Cost of Cable Internet Service

Parallelism and Perpendicularity

Support for Benchmarks MA.C.3.4.1, MA.C.3.4.2

EXAMPLES **Show that the lines with equations $y + x = 8$ and $y = -x - 3$ are parallel.**

Solution

Write each equation in slope-intercept form.

$$y + x = 8 \rightarrow y = -x + 8$$
$$y = -x - 3$$

The graphs of both equations have a slope of -1. The lines are parallel.

Show that the lines with equations $y + 2x = 5$ and $y = \frac{1}{2}x - 1$ are perpendicular.

Solution

Write each equation in slope-intercept form.
$$y + 2x = 5 \rightarrow y = -2x + 5$$
$$y = \frac{1}{2}x - 1$$

The graphs of the equations have slopes of -2 and $\frac{1}{2}$. The slopes are negative reciprocals of each other, so the lines are perpendicular.

Exercises

1. Which of the following equations has a graph that is perpendicular to the graph of $y = 2x + 5$?

   (A) $y = -2x + 2$ (B) $y = -\frac{1}{2}x - 3$ (C) $y = 3x + 5$ (D) $y = \frac{1}{2}x + 1$

2. Which of the following would NOT prove that two lines are perpendicular?

   (F) An angle formed by the intersection of the two lines measures 90 degrees.

   (G) Vertical angles formed by the intersection of the two lines are congruent.

   (H) One line is parallel to the x-axis and the other is parallel to the y-axis.

   (I) The product of the slopes of the two lines equals -1.

3. The graph of line p is shown.

   Which of the following is an equation of a line that is parallel to line p in the graph?

   (A) $-x - 4y = 8$ (C) $4y - x = 8$

   (B) $4y + x = 8$ (D) $8x + y = 4$

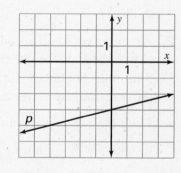

4. Describe the relationship between a line with the equation $6x - 2y + 2 = 0$ and a line with the equation $3y + x + 6 = 0$. Justify your answer.

Step Functions

Support for Benchmark MA.E.1.4.1

> **Step functions** are often used to describe real-world situations. When an open circle is used on a graph, it indicates that the value is at the end of a "step." In the example below, a package that weighs 2 pounds costs $9 to ship, not $6. A package that weighs 1.9 pounds would cost $6.

EXAMPLE The graph shows the cost of shipping a package with Speedy Ship.

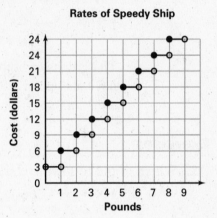

Rates of Speedy Ship

Emil is shipping one package that weighs 5.4 pounds and another package that weighs 4.8 pounds. How much, in dollars, will Emil pay to ship both packages?

Emil's first package weighs at least 5 pounds but less than 6 pounds. It will cost $18 to ship that package. Emil's second package weighs at least 4 pounds but less than 5 pounds. It will cost $15 to ship that package. It will cost $18 + $15 = $33 to ship both packages.

Exercises

Refer to the graph to answer Questions 1 and 2. The graph shows the costs associated with Arianna's long-distance phone calling plan.

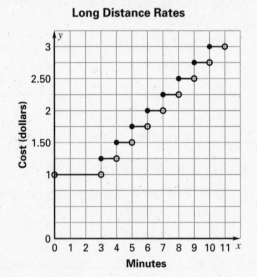

Long Distance Rates

1. How much will it cost Arianna to make a long distance call that lasts 9.5 minutes?

   (A) $2.50   (C) $3.00

   (B) $2.75   (D) $3.25

2. Arianna spent $10.75 on a lengthy phone call to her sister. If the pattern that begins after 3 minutes continues, for how many minutes did Arianna and her sister talk?

   (F) at least 31 but less than 32 minutes

   (G) exactly 39 minutes

   (H) at least 41 but less than 42 minutes

   (I) more than 45 minutes

Step Functions *(continued)*

Support for Benchmark MA.E.1.4.1

Refer to the graph to answer Questions 3 and 4. Extra Fast Shipping, has rates for both "Urgent" and "Rapid" shipments. The graph shows both rates.

3. Derrick needs to ship a package that weighs 3.6 pounds. How much **more** would it cost Derrick to send the package "Urgent" than "Rapid"?

   Ⓐ $5   Ⓒ $15

   Ⓑ $10   Ⓓ $20

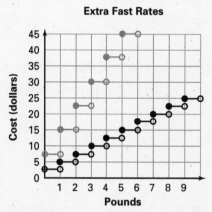

Extra Fast Rates

4. Which of the following statements is NOT true about the shipping rates?

   Ⓕ If you are shipping a package that weighs between 1 and 5 pounds, it is cheaper to use "Rapid" shipping.

   Ⓖ It costs $30 to send a 3.5 pound pacage using "Urgent" shipping.

   Ⓗ It costs $15 to send a 6 pound package using "Rapid" shipping.

   Ⓘ It costs three times more to send a 1 pound package using "Urgent" shipping.

Refer to the graph to answer Questions 5 and 6. The graph shows the rates for parking in a parking garage.

5. How many dollars does it cost to park in the garage for 2 hours and 5 minutes?

6. George spends $16 dollars for parking. For how many hours did he park in the garage?

   Ⓐ more than 8

   Ⓑ exactly 6

   Ⓒ more than or equal to 4 and less than 8

   Ⓓ more than 4 and less than or equal to 8

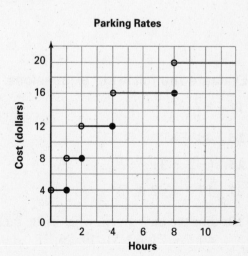

Parking Rates

FCAT Spiral Review

For use after Module 3

Write each number in scientific notation.

1. 4,310

2. 84,090

3. 6,340,000

4. 0.0724

5. 93,870,000

6. 570,810,000

7. The slope of the line shown is $-\frac{2}{3}$. What would be the slope of a line perpendicular to the line shown? Explain.

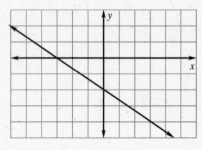

8. Explain how you know that the lines with equations $y = -4x - 5$ and $8x + 2y = 4$ are parallel.

The graph shows what a local club charges to rent its pool. Use the graph for Exercises 9 and 10.

9. What would be the cost to rent the pool for $4\frac{1}{2}$ hours?

10. Mrs. Yee only wants to spend $60 on the pool rental. What is the maximum time she and her guests can use the pool?

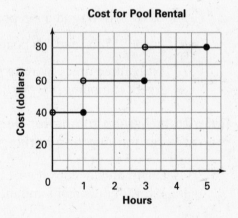

Evaluate the following expressions.

11. $-\frac{1}{9}(3^2) + 10$

12. $\left(-5\frac{2}{3} + 1\frac{1}{3}\right) + 4\frac{1}{3}$

13. $48 \div (5^2 - 1) - 3$

14. $20 + (-4)^2 - 5 \cdot 7$

15. $(-2 - 1)^2 \div 2$

16. $(4 + 6)^2 - (3 \cdot 25)$

17. $17 + (-2 + 6)^2 - 33$

18. $(9.25 + 11.75) \div (2.5^2 - 1.25)$

19. For the data given, what is the range? What is the median?
40, 26, 25, 62, 51, 19, 25, 38

Rewriting Formulas

Support for Benchmark MA.D.2.4.2

EXAMPLE The formula $ax^2 + bx + c = 0$ is known as the quadratic equation. Solve the quadratic equation for the variable b.

Solution

$ax^2 + bx + c = 0$ Write the original equation.

$bx = -ax^2 - c$ Isolate bx on one side of the equation.

$b = \dfrac{1}{x}(-ax^2 - c)$ Divide both sides of the equation by x.

$b = -ax - \dfrac{c}{x}$ Simplify.

Solving the quadratic equation for b gives $b = -ax - \dfrac{c}{x}$.

Exercises

1. The formula for converting degrees Fahrenheit to degrees Celsius is $C = \dfrac{5}{9}(F - 32)$. Solve the equation for F.

2. Which of the following equations is equivalent to $R = 500 - 5f$?

   (A) $f = 100 - \dfrac{R}{5}$ (B) $f = 500 - 5R$ (C) $f = 100 - R$ (D) $f = 5R + 500$

3. The formula $PV = nRT$ is the Ideal Gas Law. The variable P represents pressure in atmospheres, V represents the volume of the gas in liters, n is the number of moles, R is a constant, and T is temperature in Kelvins.

   Which of the following equations is NOT equivalent to $PV = nRT$?

   (F) $V = \dfrac{nRT}{P}$ (G) $P = \dfrac{V}{nRT}$ (H) $T = \dfrac{PV}{nR}$ (I) $n = \dfrac{PV}{RT}$

4. Adrian wants to know how much it will cost to run his new dishwasher. He found a formula for the cost of operating an electrical device, but it is in terms of time t.

   $t = \dfrac{1{,}000C}{Wc}$

   In the formula, t represents the number of hours, C is the cost of operation, W is the number of watts, and c is the cost in cents per kilowatt-hour. How can Adrian rewrite the formula to solve for the cost in dollars, C? Show your work or explain in words how you got your answer.

5. Which of the following equations is equivalent to $y = 3x - \dfrac{1}{3}$?

   (A) $\dfrac{1}{3}y - \dfrac{1}{9} = x$ (B) $y + \dfrac{1}{9} = x$ (C) $y - \dfrac{1}{9} = x$ (D) $\dfrac{1}{3}y + \dfrac{1}{9} = x$

Angles in Triangles

Support for Benchmarks MA.B.1.4.2, MA.C.2.4.1

EXAMPLE Which theorem from geometry can be used to find $m\angle G$ in the diagram below?

From the Exterior Angle Theorem,
you know that $m\angle G + m\angle H = 120°$.
$\angle H$ is a right angle. So $m\angle H = 90°$.
Substitute and solve for $m\angle G$.
$m\angle G + m\angle H = 120°$
$\quad m\angle G + 90° = 120°$
$\qquad\qquad m\angle G = 30°$

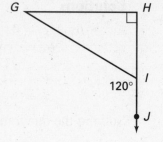

Exercises

1. Triangle *DEF* is an equilateral triangle.

    What is the measure of $\angle DEF$?

    (A) 60°   (C) 120°

    (B) 90°   (D) 180°

2. What is the measure, in degrees, of $\angle KLM$?

    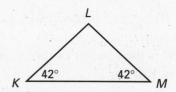

3. Oscar is making brackets to support a shelf. The brackets are right triangles. Oscar knows that two of the angle measures are 90° and 45°. What is the measure of the third angle?

    (F) 135°   (G) 90°   (H) 55°   (I) 45°

4. To widen a highway at an intersection, the highway department will use a piece of land shaped like a triangle. The survey crew has determined the measures of two exterior angles, as shown.

    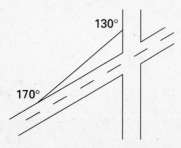

    Part A Determine the measures of the interior angles adjacent to the exterior angles whose measures are known.

    Part B What is the measure of the third interior angle? Explain how you got your answer.

Congruent Triangles

Support for Benchmarks MA.B.2.4.1, MA.C.1.4.1, MA.C.2.4.1

EXAMPLE In the diagram, $\triangle ABC \cong \triangle DEF$.
Find the length of $\overline{DE}$.

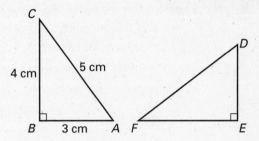

Solution

Use the statement $\triangle ABC \cong \triangle DEF$ to
write three statements about the lengths
of the sides of the triangles:

$$AB = DE \qquad BC = EF \qquad AC = DF$$

According to the diagram, $AB = 3$ cm,
so $DE = 3$ cm.

Exercises

1. In the diagram, $\overline{JK}$ is parallel to $\overline{MN}$
   and $\overline{JL} \cong \overline{ML}$.

   Show that $\triangle JKL$ is congruent to
   $\triangle MNL$. Explain in words, or provide a
   proof.

   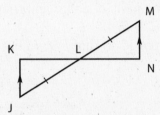

2. Rita has two identical corner cabinets with triangular bases. One
   angle of the first cabinet's base measures 90°. An angle on the
   second cabinet's base measures 45°. What are all three measures of
   both cabinets' bases?

   (A) 45°, 90°, 90°   (B) 45°, 45°, 90°   (C) 45°, 55°, 90°   (D) 45°, 90°, 180°

3. In the triangles shown, $\overline{RS}$ is congruent to $\overline{WV}$ and $\overline{ST}$ is congruent
   to $\overline{VX}$. In addition, $\angle RST$ is congruent to $\angle WVX$.

   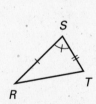 

   Which of the following proves that $\triangle RST$ is congruent to $\triangle VWX$?

   (F) If all three sides of two triangles are congruent, the triangles are congruent.

   (G) If all three angles of two triangles are congruent, the triangles are congruent.

   (H) If two sides and one angle of one triangle are congruent to two sides and one
       angle of another triangle, the triangles are congruent.

   (I) If two sides and the included angle of one triangle are congruent to the
       corresponding sides and angle of another triangle, the triangles are congruent.

Applying Congruent Triangles

Support for Benchmark MA.C.2.4.1

EXAMPLE In the diagram, $\overline{AE}$ measures 12 centimeters and $\overline{BD}$ measures 12 centimeters. The measures of two angles are given: $m\angle BAE = m\angle CBD = 22.6°$.

If $DC = 5$ centimeters, what is ED?

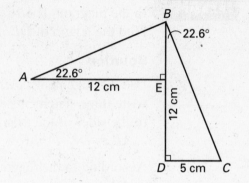

Solution

Examine the given information.
$m\angle BAE = m\angle CBD = 22.6°$

$m\angle AEB = m\angle BDC = 90°$
$AE = BD = 12$ centimeters

By the Angle-Side-Angle Theorem, $\triangle ABE \cong \triangle BCD$.
Corresponding parts of congruent triangles have the same length.
So, $DC = BE = 5$.
Subtract 5 from 12 to find ED; $ED = 7$.

Exercises

1. $\triangle MNO$ is congruent to $\triangle PNO$. As shown, $\overline{NO} \perp \overline{MP}$.

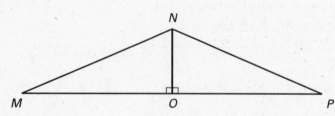

If $m\angle NMO$ is 27°, what is the measure of $\angle MNP$?

Ⓐ 153°   Ⓑ 126°   Ⓒ 116°   Ⓓ 63°

2. An artist groups three identical triangular canvases together as shown in the diagram. Each canvas contains a right angle.

If $YU = XW = WU = 10$ cm and VU is 7.1 cm, what is the length of $\overline{XY}$?

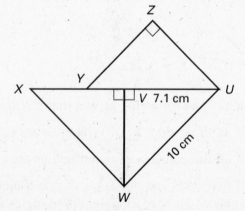

Applying Congruent Triangles *(continued)*

Support for Benchmark MA.C.2.4.1

3. Two sets of bleachers face each other across a field. The corresponding dimensions of the bleachers are equal, so the triangles in the diagram are congruent.

If the distance from point A to point B is 300 feet, what is the distance, in feet, from point C to point D?

4. In the diagram, $\angle ABE \cong \angle CBE$ and $\angle ADE \cong \angle CDE$.

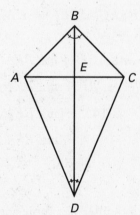

If the length of $\overline{EC}$ is 9 inches, what is the length of $\overline{AC}$?

- Ⓕ 9 inches
- Ⓖ 13.5 inches
- Ⓗ 18 inches
- Ⓘ 20.5 inches

5. Two triangular plots of land are adjacent to one another. $\overline{JK} \parallel \overline{LM}$ and $\overline{KL} \parallel \overline{JM}$. $JK = 18$ meters, $JM = 24$ meters.

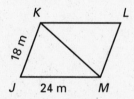

Part A Explain in geometric terms why $\triangle JKM$ is congruent to $\triangle LMK$.

Part B Explain how to find KL and LM.

Part C How many seconds would it take you to walk around the perimeter of $JKLM$ at a rate of 2 meters per second.

Special Triangles

Support for Benchmarks MA.C.1.4.1, MA.C.2.4.1

EXAMPLE In the diagram, $\triangle EBC$ is isosceles with legs $\overline{BE}$ and $\overline{BC}$ congruent. $\overline{AB} \| \overline{EC}$, $\overline{BD}$ bisects $\angle EBC$, $m\angle CBD = 20°$, and $m\angle BAE$ is 75°. What is $m\angle BEA$?

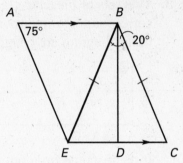

Solution

$\overline{BD}$ bisects $\angle EBC$, so $m\angle EBC = 2(m\angle CBD) = 2(20°) = 40°$.

$\triangle EBC$ is isosceles, so $\angle BEC \cong \angle BCE$.

So, $m\angle BEC = \frac{1}{2}(180 - 40) = 70°$.

Because $\overline{AB} \| \overline{EC}$, $\angle BEC \cong \angle ABE$ by the Corresponding Angles Postulate, so $m\angle ABE = 70°$.

$m\angle BAE + m\angle ABE + m\angle BEA = 180°$	Triangle Sum Theorem
$75° + 70° + m\angle BEA = 180°$	Substitute angle measurements.
$145° + m\angle BEA = 180°$	Simplify.
$m\angle BEA = 135°$	Subtract 145° from each side.

Exercises

1. Figure $LMNOPQ$ is a regular hexagon with all sides congruent. The measure of each angle of the hexagon is 120°.

   What is the measure of $\angle MNP$? Explain your answer.

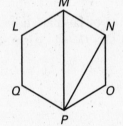

2. $\triangle FGH$ is an isosceles triangle where $\overline{FG} \cong \overline{GH}$. The measure of $\angle GHI$ is 138°.

   What is the measure, in degrees, of $\angle FGH$? Explain your answer.

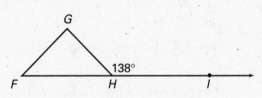

3. In the diagram, $\overline{QR} \cong \overline{TS}$ and $\overline{SU} \perp \overline{UT}$. Point S is the midpoint of $\overline{RP}$ and point P is the midpoint of $\overline{SU}$.

   If $m\angle QRP$ is 30° and $m\angle RQP$ is 60°, show that $\triangle PRQ$ is congruent to $\triangle UST$. Explain your answer.

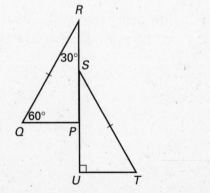

Triangles on Coordinate Grids

Support for Benchmarks MA.C.3.4.1, MA.C.3.4.2

EXAMPLE A triangle congruent to △ABC will be graphed on the grid. The new triangle will be named △DBC, and it will share side BC with △ABC. Assuming that D and A are different points, what are the coordinates of point D?

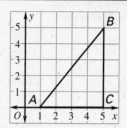

Solution

The new triangle, △DBC, can be graphed by reflecting △ABC over the line x = 5.
Because AC = 4, CD will also equal 4.
The coordinates of point D are (9, 0).

Exercises

1. △DEF has been graphed on a coordinate grid. Its coordinates are D(0, 0), E(1, 5), and F(4, 1). Is △DEF a right triangle? Support your answer by showing your work.

2. Determine the lengths of all three sides of △GHI. Be sure to show your work.

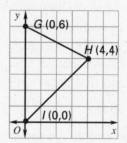

3. In the diagram, point R of △RST lies on $\overleftrightarrow{MN}$. The coordinates of the points are R(0, 0), S(5, 1), T(0, −4), M(2, 2), and N(−2, −2).

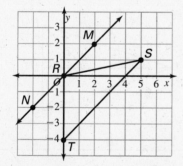

   If m∠NRT = 45° degrees, what is the measure, in degrees, of ∠RTS?

4. △LMN has been graphed on a coordinate grid. Its coordinates are L(0, 0), M(0, 8), and N(4, 0). What is the midpoint of $\overline{MN}$?

   (A) (0, 4)   (B) (2, 4)   (C) (4, 4)   (D) (4, 2)

Perpendicular and Angle Bisectors

Support for Benchmark MA.C.2.4.1

EXAMPLE   In the diagram at the right, $\overline{BD}$ bisects $\angle ABC$.
If $m\angle ADC = 140°$, what is the measure of
$\angle ABD$?

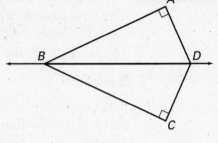

Solution

In $\triangle ABD$ and $\triangle CBD$, $m\angle ABD = m\angle CBD$
and $m\angle BAD = m\angle BCD$. The remaining
angles in $\triangle ABD$ and $\triangle CBD$ must also have
the same measures: $m\angle ADB = m\angle CDB = 70°$,
because $m\angle ADC = 140°$.

$m\angle ABD = 20°$ because the sum of the angles of a triangle is $180°$.

Exercises

1. Raul needs to determine the perimeter of an
   archeological site, designated *LMNO* as
   shown. The site has been divided into three
   sections. From survey measurements, Raul
   knows that $\overline{LM}$ and $\overline{MN}$ both measure
   50 meters. He also knows that $\overline{LP}$ and $\overline{PN}$
   measure 20 meters and that the length of
   $\overline{NO}$ is $\frac{4}{5}$ the length of $\overline{MN}$.

   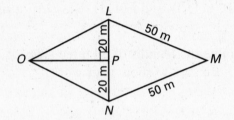

   Part A What are the lengths, in meters, of $\overline{NO}$ and $\overline{LO}$? Justify
              your answer.
   Part B What is the perimeter, in meters, of the site? Show your
              work.

2. In the diagram at right, $\overline{QU}$ is the perpendicular bisector
   of $\overline{RS}$. The measure of $\angle RQS$ is 36° and the measure of
   $\angle QRS$ is 72°. Also, $\overline{RT} \perp \overline{TS}$. What is the measure, in
   degrees, of $\angle QRT$?

   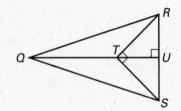

3. In the diagram, $\overline{AB} \cong \overline{BC} \cong \overline{BE}$. Based **only**
   on the information in the diagram, which of the
   following statements is true?

   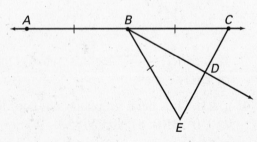

   Ⓐ $\triangle BCE$ is isosceles.

   Ⓑ $\overrightarrow{BD}$ bisects $\angle CBE$.

   Ⓒ $\overline{CD} \cong \overline{DE}$

   Ⓓ $\triangle BCE$ is equilateral.

Name _____   Date _____

Equations, Expressions, and Inequalities

Support for Benchmark MA.D.2.4.2

EXAMPLE 1 The Chos are moving to Tampa and buying a house. The moving costs will be about $2,500. They have also budgeted $3,000 for new appliances. The maximum amount they want to spend on the move and the house is $110,000. Which of the following inequalities represents the amount h that the Chos are willing to spend on their new house?

(A) $h \geq 110,000 - 2,500 - 3,000$ (C) $h < 110,000 - 2,500 - 3,000$

(B) $h > 110,000 - 2,500 - 3,000$ (D) $h \leq 110,000 - 2,500 - 3,000$

First, try to state the problem in one sentence.

The cost of the house, the move, and the appliances can total no more than $110,000.

In other words, the total cost must be less than or equal to $110,000.

$h + 2,500 + 3,000 \leq 110,000$

The answer is **D**.

EXAMPLE 2 For planting trees, a landscaper charges $25 per tree and $30 per hour for labor. Write an equation that can be used to determine the cost, c, based on the number of trees planted, t, and the hours of labor, h, needed to plant the trees. How much will it cost to plant 8 trees if it takes 6 hours to plant them?

Solution

Use a verbal model to write an algebra equation. Then substitute.

$$\boxed{\text{Cost}} = \$25 \cdot \boxed{\text{Number of trees}} + \$30 \cdot \boxed{\text{Hours of labor}}$$

$c = 25t + 30h$
$\quad = 25(8) + 30(6)$
$\quad = 380$

So, it costs $380 to plant 8 trees in 6 hours.

Exercises

1. To stay within budget, a law firm must spend less than $8,000 on new furniture. They need to buy 2 tables, each with cost t, and 20 chairs, each with cost c. Which of the following inequalities represents the amount the law firm can spend on new furniture?

(A) $8,000 > 2t + 20c$ (C) $8,000 < 2t + 20c$

(B) $8,000 \geq 2t + 20c$ (D) $8,000 \leq 2t + 20c$

Equations, Expressions, and Inequalities
(continued)

Support for Benchmark MA.D.2.4.2

2. An interior designer charges $100 for a one-hour consultation and
$60 per hour for each additional hour. The designer also charges
35¢ per mile for the number of miles driven to and from the
customer's home. Which expression below could be used to find the
cost of a consultation with the interior designer?

m = total number of miles driven
h = number of hours for the consultation

(F) $100 - 1 + 60h + 0.35m$ (H) $100 + 60h + 0.35m$

(G) $100 + 60(h - 1 + 0.35m)$ (I) $100 + 60(h - 1) + 0.35m$

3. An online music service charges $10 per month for membership and
$.79 per downloaded music file.

   Part A   Use a verbal model to write an equation that can be used to
   determine your cost, c, based on the number of months of
   membership, m, and the number of files downloaded, f.

   Part B   How much will it cost you to download 36 files if you are a
   member for 3 months? Show your work.

4. A restaurant can seat 160 people. Five-eighths of the seating is in the
main dining room. The restaurant also has a secondary dining room
and a party room. In the secondary dining room, there are 2 tables
that seat 4, a booth that seats 6, and 3 tables that seat 2. How many
people can the party room seat?

5. Emilio has 24,152 miles on the odometer of his car. He is driving
from Miami to Washington, D.C. Then he will drive the 440 miles to
Boston from Washington before returning to Miami by the same
route. Emilio predicts that by the time he returns to Miami, his
odometer will read 27,156. Which equation shows how to find the
number of miles, m, from Miami to Washington, D.C.?

(A) $m = \dfrac{27,156 - 24,152 - 440}{2}$ (C) $m = 27,156 - 24,152 - 440$

(B) $m = \dfrac{27,156 - 24,152 - 2(440)}{2}$ (D) $m = 2(27,156 - 24,152 - 440)$

6. Six months into the year, Keisha was promoted from assistant
manager to manager. Her salary as manager is $\frac{1}{8}$ more than her
salary as an assistant manager. As manager, Keisha makes
$3,240 per month. How much money did Keisha make per month
as an assistant manager?

FCAT Spiral Review

For use after Module 4

Solve for *x*.

1. $180 - 9y = 3x$

2. $32 + 4y = 8x$

3. $5(3x + 6y) = 60$

4. $3(8y + 12) = 4(x + y)$

5. $6(4 + 3x) = 3(y - 4)$

6. $4(x + y) = 12(2x - 30)$

Solve for the variable indicated.

7. $y = mx + b$; solve for b

8. $P = 2l + 2w$; solve for l

9. $V = \pi r^2 h$; solve for h

10. $V = \frac{1}{3}lwh$; solve for l

11. $Ax + By = C$; solve for y

12. $A = P(1 + rt)$; solve for t

13. $A = \frac{1}{2}h(b_1 + b_2)$; solve for b_1

14. $c^2 = a^2 + b^2$; solve for a

Determine if the triangles are congruent. Write *congruent* or *not congruent*.

15.

16.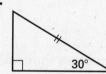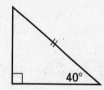

17. Jessica and Byron each work weekly jobs. Jessica works 35 hours each week and makes \$394.80 each week before taxes. Byron works 22 hours each week and makes \$275.66 each week before taxes. How much more per hour does Byron make than Jessica?

18. Mr. Ramirez is looking at his investments. He determines that stocks make up 75% of his investments, while bonds make up the remaining 25%. If Mr. Ramirez wanted to display his investments in a circle graph, what would the angle measure for the stocks section be?

19. To provide flowers for a banquet, a florist charges \$24.50 for each flower arrangement plus a delivery fee of \$35. Write an equation for the total cost c of an order for n flower arrangements delivered by the florist. Find the cost if 20 arrangements are delivered to the banquet.

Solving Linear Inequalities

Support for Benchmark MA.D.2.4.2

> Addition and subtraction have no effect on the inequality symbol in a linear inequality. However, if you multiply or divide by a negative number, you must reverse the inequality symbol.

EXAMPLE 1 **Solve $64 < 8 - 4x$.**

$64 < 8 - 4x$	
$64 - 8 < -4x$	Subtract 8 from both sides of the equation.
$56 < -4x$	Subtract 8 from 64.
$\dfrac{56}{-4} > x$	Divide both sides of the equation by -4. Reverse the inequality symbol.
$-14 > x$	Divide 56 by -4.
$x < -14$	Restate the inequality.

The solution is $x < -14$.

EXAMPLE 2 **Solve the compound inequality and graph the solution.**

a. $2 \le 3x + 2 < 11$ **b.** $-x + 1 > 7 \ or \ 2x + 1 \ge -3$

Solution

$2 \le 3x + 2 < 11$ $-x + 1 > 7 \quad or \quad 2x + 1 \ge -3$

$0 \le 3x < 9$ $-x > 6 \quad or \qquad 2x \ge -4$

$0 \le x < 3$ $x < -6 \ or \qquad x \ge -2$

Exercises

1. If both of the inequalities below are true, which statement describes the value of y?

$$y < 1{,}500 + 2{,}000 \qquad 2{,}000 \le y + 1{,}500$$

(A) The value of y is greater than or equal to 500 but less than 3,500.

(B) The value of y is greater than 500 but less than or equal to 3,500.

(C) The value of y is greater than 500 but less than 3,500.

(D) The value of y is greater than 500.

Solving Linear Inequalities *(continued)*
Support for Benchmark MA.D.2.4.2

2. The high school band needs to make at least $750 during their car wash fundraiser in order to travel to Tallahassee for a regional contest. The band director estimates that the band will wash 125 cars during their weekend car wash. Which of the following inequalities expresses how much the band should charge for a car wash c to meet or exceed their fundraising goal?

 Ⓕ $c > 6$ Ⓖ $c \geq 6$ Ⓗ $c \geq 16$ Ⓘ $c > 16$

3. Which of the following is the solution of the inequality $20 > 5x + 5$?

 Ⓐ $x > 3$ Ⓑ $x < 3$ Ⓒ $x > 5$ Ⓓ $x < 5$

4. Traci has $120 of birthday money to spend. She has found a jacket she wants that costs $75. Traci also likes T-shirts that cost $12 each. Which inequality shows how many T-shirts Traci can buy with her birthday money if she also buys the jacket?

 Ⓕ $120 \geq 75 + 12T$ Ⓖ $120 \leq 75 + 12T$ Ⓗ $120 + 75 \leq 12T$ Ⓘ $\frac{120}{T} \geq 75 + 12$

5. Greenville is 20 miles from Belton and 40 miles from Lakeview. You wish to estimate the distance d between Belton and Lakeview.

 Part A What is the smallest value d could be?

 Part B What is the largest value d could be?

 Part C Write a compound inequality that describes all the possible values of d.

6. What is the solution of the inequality $3x + 1 > 15x - 11$?

 Ⓐ $x < -1$ Ⓑ $x < -\frac{5}{6}$ Ⓒ $x < 1$ Ⓓ $x > -\frac{5}{6}$

7. Solve the compound inequality $-10 < 2x + 6 \leq 10$ and graph the solution. Show your work and justify each step.

8. Solve the compound inequality $-3x - 2 < 1$ *or* $2x + 1 < -7$ and graph the solution. Show your work and justify each step.

9. Sam is taking his wife to dinner and a movie. The inequality $75 \geq 1.2d + 12$ represents how much Sam can spend on the evening (d is the cost of dinner). How much can Sam spend on dinner?

 Ⓕ less than $52.50   Ⓗ no more than $62.50

 Ⓖ no more than $52.50   Ⓘ less than $75.60

Triangle Inequalities

Support for Benchmark MA.C.1.4.1

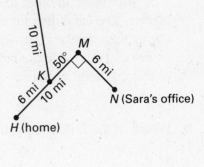

EXAMPLE Francisco and Sara Vallejo both drive 16 miles from their home to work. Their routes are shown.

In a straight-line distance, who works farther from home, Francisco or Sara? Show your work.

Solution

HL represents the distance between home and Francisco's office. *HN* represents the distance between home and Sara's office.

Because *MN* = *HK* = 6 mi, *MN* ≅ *HK*.
Because *HM* = *KL* = 10 mi, *HM* ≅ *KL*.

$m\angle HKL + m\angle MKL = 180°$ Linear Pair Postulate
$m\angle HKL + 50° = 180°$ Substitute for $m\angle HKL$.
$m\angle HKL = 130°$ Subtract 50° from each side.

∠*HMN* is a right angle, so $m\angle HMN = 90°$.

Since 130° > 90°, $m\angle HKL > m\angle HMN$.
By the Hinge Theorem, *HL* > *HN*.

Therefore, Francisco's office is farther from home.

Exercises

1. Using the flight paths described below, determine who is farther from the airport. Explain your reasoning.

   Your flight: 150 miles due west, then 70 miles N 30° W
   Your friend's flight: 150 miles due north, then 70 miles N 40°E

2. In the diagram, $\overline{DE} \cong \overline{GF}$, $m\angle DEG = 41°$ and $m\angle EGF = 90°$.

   If *DE* = 8 and *EG* = 6, which of the following could be true?

   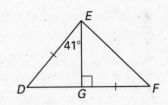

   A *DG* = 12   **C** *DG* = 8
   B *EF* = 5   **D** *EF* = 10

3. In the diagram, $\overline{ZW} \cong \overline{YZ}$ and *XY* > *WX*.

   Show that $m\angle XZY > m\angle WZX$. Show your work, explain in words, or provide a proof.

   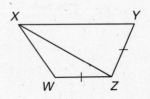

Finding an Unknown Angle

Support for Benchmark MA.B.1.4.2

EXAMPLE A floor in a large office building has four sides, but it is not rectangular. Three of the interior angles measure 100 degrees, 89 degrees, and 110 degrees. What is the measure of the fourth angle?

Solution

Let $x°$ represent the measure of the fourth angle.

$100° + 89° + 110° + x° = 360°$	Sum of measures of interior $\angle$s of a quadrilateral is 360°.
$299 + x = 360$	Simplify.
$x = 61$	Subtract 299 from each side.

The measure of the fourth angle is 61°.

Exercises

1. In $\triangle ABC$, $m\angle B = 90°$ and $m\angle C$ is 9 degrees greater than twice the measure of $\angle A$. What is $m\angle A$?

   (A) 72° (B) 63° (C) 45° (D) 27°

2. The diagram shows a viewing platform that has been built at the edge of a deep valley. If $m\angle DEF = 140°$, $m\angle FGH = 95°$ and $m\angle GHD = 80°$, then what is $m\angle EFG$? Show your work or explain in words how you found the measure.

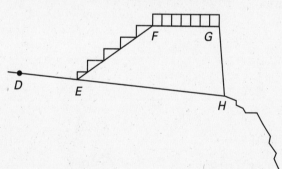

3. The diagram shows part of the Parker's house. The support, $\overline{EF}$, is parallel to $\overline{DG}$ and $\overline{BA}$. In addition, $\overline{BD} \perp \overline{DG}$, $\overline{BC} \cong \overline{DC}$, and $m\angle DEF = 125°$. What is $m\angle BCD$? Show your work or explain in words how you found the measure.

Finding an Unknown Angle *(continued)*

Support for Benchmark MA.B.1.4.2

4. The diagram below shows the top corner of a barn door. In the diagram, $\overline{QR} \perp \overline{SR}$. If $m\angle SRT = 50°$, what is the measure, in degrees, of $\angle QRT$?

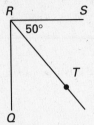

5. The map below shows the intersections of Nelson and Alta Mesa with the highway.

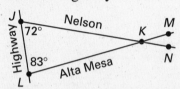

   What is the measure of $\angle MKN$?

   (F) 15°   (G) 25°   (H) 65°   (I) 155°

6. Eduardo's vegetable garden is situated in the corner of his yard, as shown. Triangle *TUV* is NOT part of the garden.

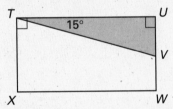

   If $m\angle UTV = 15°$, what is the measure of $\angle TVW$?

   (A) 180°   (B) 165°   (C) 105°   (D) 90°

7. The quadrilateral shown is a tile used in a repeating pattern. In the quadrilateral, $\overline{BC} \parallel \overline{AD}$ and $\overline{BA} \parallel \overline{CD}$. If $m\angle BCD$ is 9 degrees less than half the measure of $\angle ABC$, what is $m\angle BCD$? Show your work and justify each step.

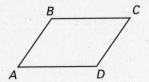

Properties of Parallelograms

Support for Benchmarks MA.C.1.4.1, MA.C.3.4.2

EXAMPLE In the diagram, *PQRU* and *RSTU* are parallelograms. Show that $\overline{PQ} \cong \overline{ST}$.

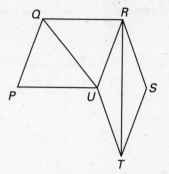

Solution

In parallelogram *PQRU*, $\overline{PQ} \cong \overline{RU}$ because opposite sides of a parallelogram are congruent.

In parallelogram *RSTU*, $\overline{RU} \cong \overline{ST}$ because opposite sides of a parallelogram are congruent.

$\overline{PQ} \cong \overline{RU}$ and $\overline{RU} \cong \overline{ST}$, so by the Transitive Property of Congruence, $\overline{PQ} \cong \overline{ST}$.

Exercises

1. Quadrilateral *ABCD* is a parallelogram.

Which of the following statements is NOT true?

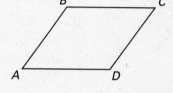

(A) $\overline{AD} \parallel \overline{BC}$ (C) $m\angle ADC + m\angle DAB = 180°$

(B) $\overline{AB} \cong \overline{DC}$ (D) $\angle ABC \cong \angle DCB$

2. Parallelogram *VWXY* has been partially graphed on the coordinate grid.

What are the coordinates of vertex *V*? Show your work and explain your reasoning.

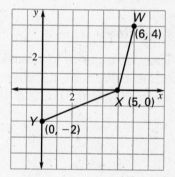

3. In the diagram, $\overline{MN} \cong \overline{OL}$ and $\angle MNL \cong \angle OLN$.

Prove that Quadrilateral *LMNO* is a parallelogram. Show your work and justify each step.

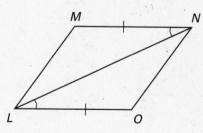

Interpreting Venn Diagrams

Support for Benchmark MA.E.1.4.1

EXAMPLE Alex, Bridget, and Sam work at the same furniture store. Their sales (in dollars) for the week are shown in the Venn diagram at the right. Use the Venn diagram to answer questions a and b.

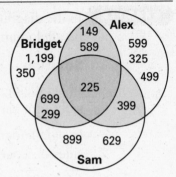

a. What was Alex's highest sale of the week?

    (A) $599   (C) $399

    (B) $589   (D) $225

b. How many sale prices did Bridget and Sam have in common?

Solution

a. Alex's sales are all in the circle labeled Alex. The sale prices in Alex's circle are $599, $325, $499, $399, $225, $149, and $589. The highest sale is $599. The answer is A.

b. Bridget and Sam's common sale prices appear where their two circles overlap. The bottom of Bridget's circle overlaps the top of Sam's circle. The prices that appear in that section are $699, $299, and $225. Bridget and Sam have 3 sale prices in common.

Exercises

Three groups of students from all over Miami compared their home telephone number prefixes. The results are shown in the Venn diagram. Use the diagram to answer questions 1 and 2.

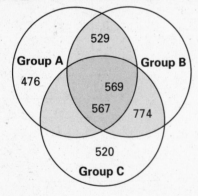

1. Which groups have the prefix 774 in common?

    (A) Group A and Group B   (C) Group A and Group C

    (B) Group B and Group C   (D) Groups A, B, and C

2. Which group did NOT have the prefix 774?

Interpreting Venn Diagrams *(continued)*

Support for Benchmark MA.E.1.4.1

A real estate agent is comparing 3 clients and the homes they toured. She has recorded the square footage of the homes that the Jordans, the Nguyens, and the LeBlancs toured in a Venn diagram. Use the diagram to answer questions 3 and 4.

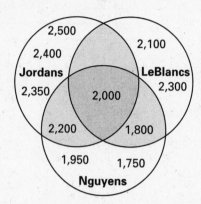

3. What was the square footage of the home that all 3 clients toured?

4. What was the square footage of the largest home that more than one client toured?

   Ⓕ 2,000 square feet   Ⓖ 2,100 square feet   Ⓗ 2,200 square feet   Ⓘ 2,500 square feet

Maria, Claudia, and their father played 3 games at the bowling alley. Their scores are shown in the Venn diagram. Use the diagram to answer questions 5 and 6.

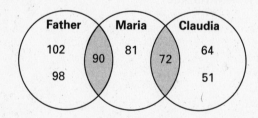

5. Why are the circles for Father and Claudia NOT overlapping?

   Ⓐ The circles are in order of highest to lowest score, so Father's circle appears first and Claudia's appears last.

   Ⓑ The circles do not need to overlap because Maria's circle overlaps both other circles.

   Ⓒ Claudia played 3 games against Maria and no games against Father.

   Ⓓ Claudia and Father do not have any bowling scores in common.

6. What is the mean score for the entire data set?

Name _____ Date _____

Properties of Quadrilaterals

Support for Benchmarks MA.C.1.4.1, MA.C.3.4.1, MA.C.3.4.2

EXAMPLE Quadrilateral *ABCD* is shown on the
coordinate grid. Prove that *ABCD* is a rhombus.

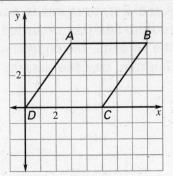

Solution

A quadrilateral is a rhombus if it has four
congruent sides. By simply counting the squares
of the grid, you can determine that AB and DC
are both 5 units long. You can use the distance
formula to determine the lengths of DA and BC.

$DA = \sqrt{(x_2 - x_1)^2 + (y_2 - y_1)^2}$ Use the distance formula.

$DA = \sqrt{(3 - 0)^2 + (4 - 0)^2}$ Substitute known values.

$DA = \sqrt{3^2 + 4^2}$ Subtract.

$DA = \sqrt{25}$ Simplify.

$DA = 5$ Evaluate the square root of 25.

If you repeat the same steps for BC, you will find that BC is also 5.

$AB = DC = DA = BC$, so all four sides of *ABCD* are congruent.
Therefore, quadrilateral *ABCD* is a rhombus.

Exercises

1. A landscape architect is laying out the paths in a courtyard to form a
square. Three paths have already been planned, as shown in the
diagram.

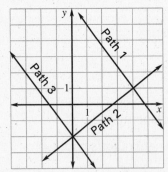

The landscape architect needs to determine the equation for the
fourth path so that the intersection of all the paths forms a square.
Which equation should be used for the fourth path?

(A) $y = \frac{3}{4}x + \frac{17}{4}$ (B) $y = \frac{2}{3}x + 4$ (C) $y = -\frac{3}{4}x + 4$ (D) $y = 5x + \frac{17}{4}$

Properties of Quadrilaterals *(continued)*

Support for Benchmarks MA.C.1.4.1, MA.C.3.4.1, MA.C.3.4.2

2. In a trapezoid, the length of the midsegment is one half the sum of the lengths of the bases. In trapezoid *LMNO,* what is the length, in inches, of midsegment $\overline{PQ}$?

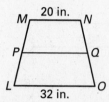

3. In the diagram shown, triangles *TUV, WUX,* and *YXV* are isosceles right triangles. $\overline{XY}$ bisects $\overline{TV}$ and $\overline{WX}$ bisects $\overline{TU}$. Prove that *TWXY* is a square.

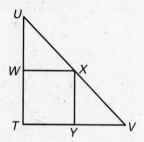

4. Quadrilateral *JKLM,* shown in the coordinate grid at the right, is a kite.

How long are sides $\overline{MJ}$ and $\overline{JK}$? How long are sides $\overline{KL}$ and $\overline{ML}$? Be sure to show your work.

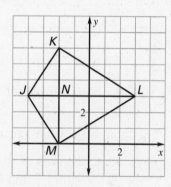

5. In the diagram below, quadrilateral *ABCD* is a parallelogram. Prove that *ABCD* is a rectangle by determining the lengths of $\overline{DB}$ and $\overline{AC}$.

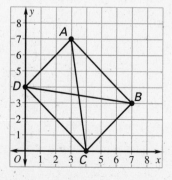

Solving for Area and Perimeter

Support for Benchmarks MA.A.4.4.1, MA.B.1.4.1, MA.B.3.4.1

> After solving a multi-step problem, you should check that your answer is reasonable. Estimation is a good way to check your answer.

EXAMPLE The diagram at the right shows a garden at a modern art museum. The garden is divided into the following regions: kite *RWXQ*, parallelogram *RSTW*, triangle *PQX*, and trapezoid *XWTV*.

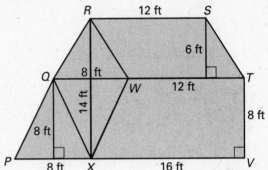

What is the total area of the garden? Use estimation to check that your answer is reasonable. Be sure to show your work or explain in words how you determined the total area and your estimate.

Solution

Find the area of each region of the garden.

Area of *RWXQ*: $\frac{1}{2}d_1 d_2 = \frac{1}{2}(8 \cdot 14) = 56$ ft^2

Area of *RSTW*: $bh = 12 \cdot 6 = 72$ ft^2

Area of *PQX*: $\frac{1}{2}bh = \frac{1}{2}(8 \cdot 8) = 32$ ft^2

Area of *XWTV*: $\frac{1}{2}h(b_1 + b_2) = \frac{1}{2}(8)(12 + 16) = 112$ ft^2

Add all four areas together.
$56 + 72 + 32 + 112 = 272$

The total area of the garden is 272 square feet.

To estimate the area of this garden, think of the garden as one simpler shape. For example, find the area of the trapezoid formed by *PRSV* to estimate the area of the garden.

$$\text{Estimate for area of } PRSV = \frac{1}{2}h\,(b_1 + b_2) = \frac{1}{2}(6 + 8)[(8 + 16) + 12]$$

$$= \frac{1}{2}(14)(36)$$

$$= 252$$

The answer of 272 square feet is reasonable.

Solving for Area and Perimeter *(continued)*

Support for Benchmarks MA.A.4.4.1, MA.B.1.4.1, MA.B.3.4.1

Exercises

1. A land developer has purchased side-by-side plots of land. In the diagram, the plots are trapezoid *ABCF* and parallelogram *FCDE*.

   What is the total area, in square feet, of the two plots of land?

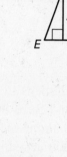

2. A rectangular park has an area of 6,400 square yards. It is crossed by two sidewalks perpendicular to one another. The shorter sidewalk measures 50 yards and is parallel to the shorter sides of the park.

   Part A What is the length, in yards, of the longer sidewalk?

   Part B The sidewalks crossing the park are 1.5 yards wide. What is the total area, in square yards, of both sidewalks?

   Part C The city has decided to resurface the existing sidewalks with paving stones. The square paving stones measure 0.5 yards on each side. How many paving stones are needed to resurface the sidewalks?

3. The shingled part of the roof shown is made up of 4 trapezoids. All the trapezoids are 9 feet high.

   What is the total area of the shingled part of the roof? Use estimation to check that your answer is reasonable. Show your work or explain in words how you calculated the area and your estimate.

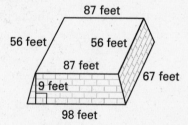

4. Eduardo is installing a picket fence around his entire yard. The diagram below shows the measurements of Eduardo's yard.

   Part A What is the total perimeter of Eduardo's yard?

   Part B If the picket fencing comes in 4-foot sections, how many sections will Eduardo need to completely fence his yard?

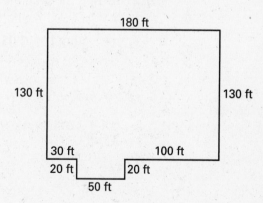

Using Percents

Support for Benchmarks MA.A.1.4.3, MA.A.1.4.4, MA.A.3.4.3

EXAMPLE 1 In a class of 25 students, 7 students wear contact lenses. What percent of the students wear contact lenses?

Solution

The fraction of students who wear contact lenses is $\frac{7}{25}$. To express $\frac{7}{25}$ as a percent, rewrite the fraction with a denominator of 100.

$$\frac{7}{25} = \frac{7 \times 4}{25 \times 4} = \frac{28}{100} = 28\%$$ 28% of the students wear contact lenses.

EXAMPLE 2 Araceli opens two savings accounts. Account A has an opening balance of $500 and earns 3% interest per year. Account B has an opening balance of $2,000 and earns 4% interest per year. At the end of one year, how much is in each account? At the end of 5 years, if no money is withdrawn and the interest rates remain constant, how much will be in Araceli's savings accounts?

Solution

Step 1 When an account earns annual interest, the formula for the amount in the account at the end of one year is $A = p(r + 1)$ where A is the amount at the end of the year, p is the amount at the beginning of the year, and r is the interest rate.

$A_a = 500(0.03 + 1)$ $A_b = 2,000(0.04 + 1)$
$ = 500(1.03)$ $ = 2,000(1.04)$
$ = 515$ $ = 2,080$

After one year, Account A has $515 and Account B has $2,080.

Step 2 To find the amount in the accounts after 5 years, use the formula $A = p(1 + r)^t$ where t is the number of years.

$A_a = 500(1 + 0.03)^5$ $A_b = 2,000(1 + 0.04)^5$
$ = 500(1.03)^5$ $ = 2,000(1.04)^5$
$ \approx 579.64$ $ \approx 2,433.31$

After 5 years, Account A has $579.64 and Account B has $2,433.31.

Using Percents *(continued)*

Support for Benchmarks MA.A.1.4.3, MA.A.1.4.4, MA.A.3.4.3

Exercises

1. Jason's apartment is $\frac{7}{8}$ the size of Kai's apartment. What is $\frac{7}{8}$ expressed as a percent?

2. Fourteen out of 56 questions on a test are multiple choice. What percent of the test is multiple choice?

   (A) 14%   (B) 25%   (C) 28%   (D) 56%

3. The Patels' restaurant bill came to $64. They gave the server an 18% tip. How much money did the Patels pay altogether?

4. Leila cut a cake into 10 pieces. She ate one piece. Then her sister and brother each ate a piece. What percent of the cake remained?

   (F) 10%   (G) 30%   (H) 70%   (I) 80%

5. Each month, Henry deposits 15% of his pay in two accounts, a regular savings account and a retirement account. Last month Henry deposited $165 in his savings account and $247.50 in his retirement account.

   Part A What is Henry's monthly pay?
   Part B What percent of Henry's monthly pay is deposited in his savings account?
   Part C What percent of Henry's monthly pay is deposited in his retirement account?

6. The original price of a T-shirt is $15.00. The sale price of the T-shirt is $4.50 less than the original price. The sale price is what percent of the original price?

   (A) 10.5%   (B) 30%   (C) 43%   (D) 70%

7. Danielle purchases an antique car for $7,500. Each year, the value of the car increases by 5%. What is the value, in dollars, of the car after 8 years? Use the formula $V = p(1 + r)^t$ where V is the value of the car, p is the amount paid for the car, r is the rate of increase expressed as a decimal, and t is the number of years.

FCAT Spiral Review

For use after Module 5

Find the measure of the unknown angle.

1. Two complementary angles whose measures are 37° and $x°$

2. Two supplementary angles whose measures are 103° and $x°$

3. Vertical angles 1 and 2 whose measures are 88° and $x°$

4. Adjacent angles in a parallelogram whose measures are 92° and $x°$

5. A triangle with angles whose measures are 35°, 59°, and $x°$

6. A quadrilateral with two right angles, an acute angle of 63° and an obtuse angle of $x°$

7. A triangle with angles whose measures are 47°, 81°, and $x°$

8. A quadrilateral with angles that are 72°, 84°, 61° and $x°$

9. A triangle with angles whose measures are 74°, 74°, and $x°$

10. A quadrilateral with angles that are 104°, 92°, 74° and $x°$

Rewrite the decimal or fraction as a percent.

11. $\frac{1}{8}$

12. 0.52

13. $\frac{2}{5}$

14. 0.019

15. $\frac{33}{50}$

16. 0.0305

17. $\frac{17}{20}$

18. 0.405

19. The picture frame shown has a width of 8 inches and inside dimensions 36 inches by 24 inches. Find the outside perimeter of the frame.

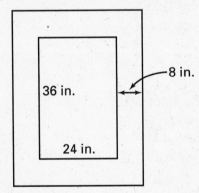

20. Find the area of the side of the building shown.

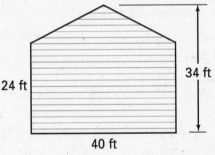

21. The vertices of $\triangle DEF$ are located at $D(1, 1)$, $E(3, 4)$ and $F(4, 1)$. Is $\triangle DEF$ an isosceles triangle? Explain your answer.

Symmetry

Support for Benchmarks MA.C.2.4.1, MA.C.3.4.1

EXAMPLE 1 The garden design shown has rotational symmetry, and can be mapped onto itself with a rotation of 90°. What are the coordinates of points *A* and *B*?

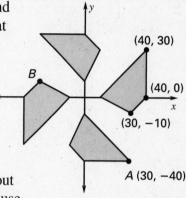

Solution

Point *A* corresponds to point (40, 30) rotated about the origin by −90°. To find the new coordinates (*x*, *y*), use (*x*, *y*) → (*y*, −*x*). So *A* has coordinates (30, −40).

Point *B* corresponds to the point (30, −10) rotated about the origin by 180°. To find the new coordinates (*x*, *y*), use (*x*, *y*) → (−*x*, −*y*). So *B* has coordinates (−30, 10).

Check that both answers appear reasonable on the graph.

EXAMPLE 2 An archaeologist uses line symmetry to recreate the design shown from a piece that had been partially destroyed. What is the overall width of the piece?

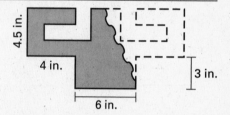

Solution

The figure has line symmetry about a vertical line bisecting the 6 inch segment. So the half of the figure to the left of the line has a width of 4 inches + $\frac{1}{2}$(6 inches), or 7 inches. The whole figure has a width twice this, or 14 inches.

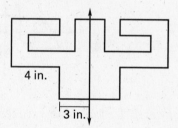

Exercises

1. The figure shown has rotational symmetry and can be mapped onto itself with a rotation of 180°. What are the coordinates of *A*?

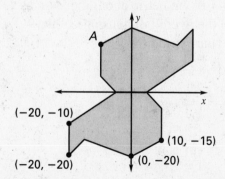

(A) (−20, 20)   (B) (−10, 15)   (C) (−15, 10)   (D) (−10, 20)

Symmetry *(continued)*

Support for Benchmarks MA.C.2.4.1, MA.C.3.4.1

2. Which angle rotation of the flower shown will NOT map the flower onto itself?

(F) 45°

(G) 90°

(H) 180°

(I) 270°

3. The *y*-axis is the line of symmetry in this design for a T-shirt logo.

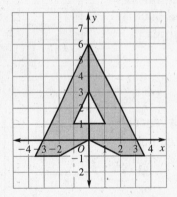

Part A List all nine vertices of the design.

Part B Suppose a small dot was added to the left side at $(-1, 3)$. What would be the corresponding point on the right side of the design? Give the formula $(x, y) \rightarrow (?, ?)$ that you used to find the answer.

4. The house shown is intended to be symmetric about the staircase, which is 4 feet wide. What will the overall dimensions of the finished floorplan be? Explain your reasoning.

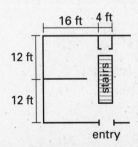

Graphs of Parabolas

Support for Benchmark MA.C.3.4.2

EXAMPLE 1 What is the axis of symmetry of the parabola?

Solution

The axis of symmetry passes through the vertex (3, 0) and runs vertically. The equation of the line of symmetry is $x = 3$.

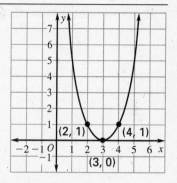

EXAMPLE 2 You want to extend the parabola above and plot the point (6, 9) on the right side of the parabola. What is the corresponding point of the left side of the parabola?

Solution

The axis of symmetry is $x = 3$. The point (6, 9) is 3 units to the right of the axis, so the corresponding point will be 3 units to the left of the line $x = 3$ with the same y-value, or (0, 9).

EXAMPLE 3 The graphs of two parabolas are shown. How would you translate the graph of $y = x^2$ to obtain the graph of $y = x^2 + 4x + 5$?

Solution

Shift the graph of $y = x^2$ 2 units left and 1 unit up. Check that all the coordinates obey the rule $(x, y) \rightarrow (x - 2, y + 1)$.

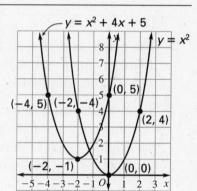

Exercises

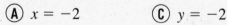

1. Tell which equation describes the axis of symmetry of the parabola.

   (A) $x = -2$ (C) $y = -2$

   (B) $x = 3$ (D) $y = 3$

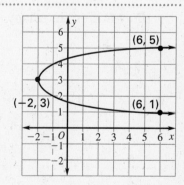

Graphs of Parabolas *(continued)*

Support for Benchmark MA.C.3.4.2

2. A student plotted the right side of a parabola.

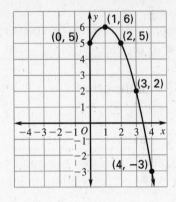

To draw the left side, what would the x-value be when $y = -3$?

(F) -4

(G) -3

(H) -2

(I) -1

3. The graph shows the height of a ball dropped from a height of 80 meters after t seconds. The graph is the right half of a parabola with a vertex of (0, 80).

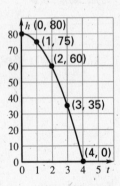

Suppose the ball is launched upward from the ground instead, reaching a maximum height of 80 meters. To graph this situation, the original graph is shifted right 4 units and the missing half of the parabola is filled in symmetrically.

Part A What is the new vertex? What point does it represent for the ball?

Part B For how many seconds is the ball in the air?

Name _____ Date _____

Transformations

Support for Benchmarks MA.C.2.4.1, MA.C.3.4.1

EXAMPLE 1 The segment $\overline{AB}$ has been transformed in three different ways. In each case, describe the transformation in words. Then describe it with an expression of the form $(x, y) \rightarrow (?, ?)$.

Solution

To form $\overline{A'B'}$, rotate $\overline{AB}$ by 90° about the origin.

$(x, y) \rightarrow (-y, x)$

To form $\overline{A''B''}$, reflect $\overline{AB}$ over the x-axis.

$(x, y) \rightarrow (x, -y)$

To form $\overline{A'''B'''}$, translate $\overline{AB}$ right 4 units and up 1 unit.

$(x, y) \rightarrow (x + 4, y + 1)$

EXAMPLE 2 In Example 1, suppose $\overline{AB}$ is reflected over the line $y = x$. What are the new coordinates A' and B'?

Solution

Use the transformation $(x, y) \rightarrow (y, x)$: $A'(4, -3)$ and $B'(3, 1)$.

Exercises

Linda plans to use quadrilateral **ABCD** as the basis for designing a stencil border. She experiments with different transformations of **ABCD**. Give the new coordinates **A′B′C′D′** for each transformation.

1. Reflect over the y-axis.
2. Translate left 5 units.
3. Rotate by 90° counterclockwise about the origin.
4. Reflect over the line $y = -x$.

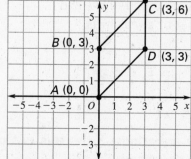

5. Sarah is analyzing a design for the yearbook logo. She wants to determine how the design with A was transformed to the design with A'.

   Part A Write an expression of the form $(x, y) \rightarrow (?, ?)$ to represent the transformation.

   Part B What rotation would produce the transformation?

   Part C Can a pair of reflections produce the transformation? Explain.

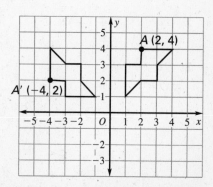

Systems of Equations and Inequalities

Support for Benchmark MA.D.2.4.2

EXAMPLE 1 Josepha is taking a pottery course. The cost is $100 for materials and instruction, and either $15 for each extra session, or $120 for unlimited access to the studio. How many extra sessions would she need to take before it became more cost-effective to pay the flat rate?

Solution

Write a system of equations. Let x = the number of extra sessions and y = the cost.

    Pay per session: $y = 100 + 15x$
    Flat rate: $y = 100 + 120 = 220$

Graph

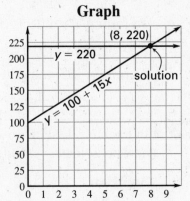

Algebra

The costs are equal when
$100 + 15x = 220$:

$$100 + 15x = 220$$
$$15x = 120$$
$$x = 8$$

If she attends more than 8 extra sessions, it is better to pay the flat rate.

EXAMPLE 2 Your club plans to sell T-shirts and sweatshirts. The club's cost is $8 for each T-shirt and $15 for each sweatshirt. You can spend $600 on the shirts. Write and graph a system of inequalities to represent the possible combinations of T-shirts and sweatshirts you can buy.

Solution

Let t = the number of T-shirts and s = the number of sweatshirts.

$$t \geq 0$$
$$s \geq 0$$
$$8t + 15s \leq 600$$

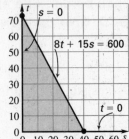

Exercises

Solve the system of linear equations. If there is not one solution, write *no solution* or *many solutions*.

1. $x - 2y = 4$
    $x - 2y = -2$

2. $x - 3y = 6$
    $2x - 6y = 12$

3. $2x - y = 1$
    $x + y = -4$

4. $x - 2y = 6$
    $-2x + y = -5$

Systems of Equations and Inequalities
(continued)

Support for Benchmark MA.D.2.4.2

5. William Ramon leaves home at 7:30 A.M. walking at 4 miles per hour. At 7:45 A.M. his brother Javier leaves home to jog along the same route, travelling at 6 miles per hour. When does Javier meet William?

(A) 7:53 a.m.   (C) 8:08 a.m.

(B) 8:00 a.m.   (D) 8:15 a.m.

6. The graph shows the distance, in kilometers, from the head of a bike trail of two bicyclists after t hours. A started at the head of the trail, and B started at the far end. How many kilometers from the head of the trail will they meet? Show your work.

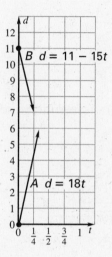

7. A printer charges $0.50 per page for color copies (c) and $0.10 per page for black and white copies (b). Rachel Carver needs to make copies of a series of reports. Each must have at least two color pages. The total cost needs to be no more than $3 per report. A graph of the constraints is shown below. What combination of pages is NOT feasible?

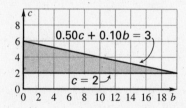

(F) 10 black and white and 4 color

(G) 7 black and white and 6 color

(H) 4 black and white and 4 color

(I) 12 black and white and 2 color

8. Use the graph in Exercise 7. If a report has 14 pages, what is the greatest possible number of color pages it can include?

FCAT Spiral Review

For use after Module 6

List the number of lines of symmetry each figure has. Also, state whether the figure has rotational symmetry.

1.

2.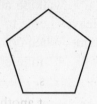

3.

4.

5.

6.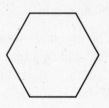

Describe the transformation as either a *reflection*, *rotation*, or *translation*.

7.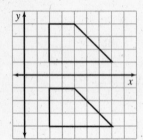

8.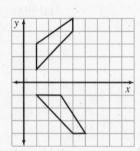

9.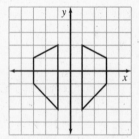

Find the point of intersection of each pair of lines.

10. $y = x$ and $x = 1$

11. $y = 2x$ and $x = 4$

12. $y = \frac{1}{2}x + 4$ and $y = 4x - 3$

13. $y = 3x - 7$ and $y = -2x + 3$

14. $y = -\frac{1}{2}x - 2$ and $y = x - 4$

15. $y = 7x - 20$ and $y = -3x + 5$

16. The segment $\overline{AB}$ has endpoints $A(-4, -3)$ and $B(8, -5)$. What are the coordinates of M, the midpoint of $\overline{AB}$?

17. A race car driver completed a lap on a track at an average speed of 160 miles per hour. What is that rate in **feet per second**?

Solve the compound inequality and graph the solution.

18. $-2 \le 3x - 5 \le 4$

19. $-4x + 7 < -9$ or $9x \le x + 8$

Proportional Reasoning

Support for Benchmarks MA.A.4.4.1, MA.B.1.4.3, MA.B.2.4.1, MA.B.3.4.1, MA.C.2.4.1, MA.C.3.4.1, MA.C.3.4.2, MA.E.1.4.3

EXAMPLE 1 Tim averages 8 minutes, 26 seconds per mile when running long distances. To estimate the time it would take Tim to run 10 miles, count the minutes first, then estimate the seconds. Then add.

Running 1 mile takes Tim 8 whole minutes, so running 10 miles would take Tim $8 \cdot 10 = 80$ minutes.

Running 1 mile also takes Tim about another 30 seconds, so running 10 miles would take Tim an additional $30 \cdot 10 = 300$ seconds. This is equal to 5 minutes.

It would take Tim about $80 + 5 = 85$ minutes, or 1 hour and 25 minutes, to run 10 miles.

EXAMPLE 2 Spruce Park is building a playground area, as shown on the map. Use the scale model of the playground to find the area of the actual playground.

The legs of the right triangle on the map measure 6 units and 10 units. Set up and solve proportions to find the actual lengths:

$$\frac{1 \text{ unit}}{5 \text{ yd}} = \frac{6 \text{ units}}{\text{actual } AB} \qquad \frac{1 \text{ unit}}{5 \text{ yd}} = \frac{10 \text{ units}}{\text{actual } AC}$$

$$AB = 30 \text{ yards} \qquad AC = 50 \text{ yards}$$

Then use the triangle area formula to find the playground's area:

$$A = \tfrac{1}{2}bh = \tfrac{1}{2}(50)(30) = 750 \text{ square yards}$$

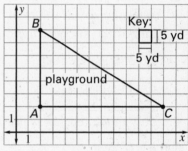

EXAMPLE 3 The Petersons are putting up a fenced enclosure for their dog. Find the length of fencing needed.

Vertical and horizontal sides

$4 + 4 + 4 + 4 = 16$ units

Slanted sides

Use the distance formula to find the length of one slanted side:

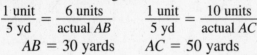
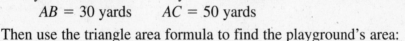

$$\sqrt{(5-2)^2 + (13-9)^2}$$
$$= \sqrt{3^2 + 4^2} = \sqrt{25} = 5 \text{ units}$$

There are 4 slanted sides: $4 \cdot 5$ units $= 20$ units

The perimeter is $16 + 20 = 36$ units. Each unit on the grid represents 2 feet, so the perimeter is $2 \cdot 36 = 72$ feet. The Petersons will need 72 feet of fencing.

Name _____ Date _____

Proportional Reasoning *(continued)*

Support for Benchmarks MA.A.4.4.1, MA.B.1.4.3, MA.B.2.4.1, MA.B.3.4.1, MA.C.2.4.1, MA.C.3.4.1, MA.C.3.4.2

Exercises

1. It takes a factory worker 2 minutes and 33 seconds to package each case of cookies. Estimate how many minutes it takes to pack 20 cases. Show your work.

2. Denise makes a map of her neighborhood on a coordinate grid. On the map, the coordinates of Denise's house are (12, 10) and the coordinates of the library are (36, 3). If each unit on the grid represents 50 feet, how far is Denise's house from the library?

   (A) 24 feet   (B) 25 feet   (C) 1,200 feet   (D) 1,250 feet

In Exercises 3 and 4, use the plans for a backyard pool shown.

3. A solar cover is going to be installed in the pool. To order the cover, the pool owner needs to know the area of the surface of the pool. What is the area?

   (F) 288 square feet   (H) 28 square feet

   (G) 48 square feet   (I) 8 square feet

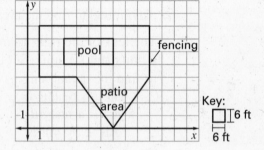

4. How much fencing is needed to enclose the area?

   (A) 12 feet   (C) 180 feet

   (B) 30 feet   (D) 192 feet

5. John wants to estimate how many worms are in the plot of land shown at the right. He tests the shaded part and finds 17 worms.

   Part A Estimate the fraction of the plot that John uses for his sample.

   Part B Use the estimate from Part A to write and solve a proportion to estimate the number of worms in the whole plot.

In a random sample of 350 high school students, 212 chose pizza as their favorite meal. Predict how many students would choose pizza at a high school of the given size.

6. 1253   7. 695   8. 149

9. A student council plans to sell baseball caps. Before ordering the caps to sell, members ask 40 randomly chosen students in each grade level what color cap they would buy. Use the results in the table and ESTIMATION STRATEGIES to predict how many caps of each color the 893 students in the school would buy. Show your work.

	red	blue	none
6th	8	12	20
7th	7	14	19
8th	8	11	21

Name _____ Date _____

Similar Triangles and Slope

Support for Benchmarks MA.B.2.4.1, MA.C.3.4.2

Vocabulary

Two triangles are called **similar triangles** if their corresponding angles are congruent and the lengths of their corresponding sides are proportional. In the diagram, $\triangle ABC$ is similar to $\triangle DEF$.

$\triangle ABC \sim \triangle DEF$

$\angle A \cong \angle D, \angle B \cong \angle E, \angle C \cong \angle F$

$\dfrac{AB}{DE} = \dfrac{BC}{EF} = \dfrac{CA}{FD}$

EXAMPLE **Two sections of a rooftop form similar triangles LMN and PQN as shown. Find the slope of $\overline{LM}$.**

Slope is the ratio of the change in y to the corresponding change in x. For $\triangle LMN$, the slope is $\dfrac{MN}{LN}$. Since

$\triangle LMN \sim \triangle PQN$, $\dfrac{MN}{LN} = \dfrac{QN}{PN} = \dfrac{9}{22}$.

The slope of $\overline{LM}$ is $\dfrac{9}{22}$.

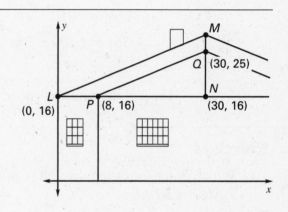

Exercises

1. In the diagram, $\triangle ABC \sim \triangle ADE$. Which coordinates is it possible for point D and point E to have?

   (A) $D(0, 16), E(12, 0)$ (C) $D(0, 8), E(12, 0)$

   (B) $D(0, 12), E(16, 0)$ (D) $D(0, 12), E(8, 0)$

2. If $\triangle ABC \sim \triangle DEF$, $AB = 2.5$, $BC = 10$, and $DE = 9$, find EF.

3. The sails of two sailboats are shown in the diagram. Triangle QRS is similar to triangle TUV. What is the slope of $\overline{QR}$? What are the coordinates of point R? Show your work.

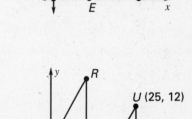

Recognizing and Using Similar Triangles

Support for Benchmark MA.C.2.4.1

EXAMPLE In a game of pool, you are trying to hit a ball against a side of the table so that it lands in the corner pocket, as shown. At what horizontal distance x must the ball hit the side?

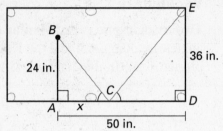

Solution

By the AA Similarity Postulate, you know that $\triangle ABC \sim \triangle DEC$. Set up and solve a proportion to find x.

$$\frac{AB}{DE} = \frac{AC}{DC}$$

$$\frac{24}{36} = \frac{x}{50 - x}$$

$$36x = 24(50 - x)$$

$$36x = 1{,}200 - 24x$$

$$x = 20$$

The ball must hit the side at a horizontal distance of 20 inches from point A.

Exercises

1. Which of the following does NOT prove that $\triangle ABC \sim \triangle DEF$?

   (A) $\angle B \cong \angle E$ (C) $\angle C \cong \angle F$

   (B) DF is two times AC (D) EF is two times AC

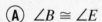

2. Which triangles are similar?

   (F) $\triangle LMN$ and $\triangle QRS$

   (G) $\triangle LMN$ and $\triangle TUV$

   (H) $\triangle QRS$ and $\triangle TUV$

   (I) $\triangle LMN$, $\triangle QRS$, and $\triangle TUV$

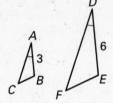

3. Given that $\triangle ABC \sim \triangle EDC$, find AB.

   (A) 14   (C) 18

   (B) 16   (D) 25

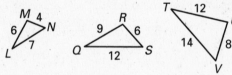

4. In a game of air hockey, you are trying to hit the puck against a wall of the table so that it lands in the goal, as shown in the diagram. At what horizontal distance x, in inches, must the puck hit the wall? Show your work.

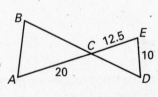

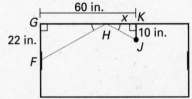

Percent of Increase and Decrease

Support for Benchmark MA.A.3.4.3

Vocabulary

A **percent of change** is a measure of how an increase or decrease in a quantity compares with the original amount:

$$\text{Percent of change } p = \frac{\text{Amount of increase or decrease}}{\text{Original amount}}$$

When the new amount is greater than the original amount, this is called a **percent of increase.** When the new amount is less than the original amount, this is called a **percent of decrease.**

EXAMPLES

What is the percent of increase from 80 to 100?

$$p = \frac{\text{Amount of increase or decrease}}{\text{Original amount}}$$

$$= \frac{100 - 80}{80}$$

$$= \frac{20}{80} = \frac{1}{4} = 25\%$$

The cost of a TV after a 20% decrease is $360. What was the original cost, c?

$$c - 0.2c = \$360$$
$$0.8c = \$360$$
$$c = \$450$$

Exercises

1. What is the percent of increase from 140 to 210?

(A) 0.5%   (B) 33.3%   (C) 50%   (D) 66.7%

2. What is the percent of decrease from 54 to 36?

(F) 25%   (G) 33.3%   (H) 50%   (I) 66.7%

3. The number of alligators at a zoo increased by 15%. If there were 20 alligators originally, how many alligators are there now?

(A) 25   (B) 23   (C) 17   (D) 3

4. A clothing store sold 62 pairs of jeans this week. This is a 24% increase from last week's sales. How many pairs of jeans did the store sell last week?

5. Jason scored 200 points in his first basketball season.
   Part A Find the number of points Jason scored in his second season if he increased his total points by 20%.
   Part B Find the number of points Jason scored in his third season if he decreased his total points from the previous season by 5%. Show your work.

6. If the percent of increase is 120%, then the new amount is what percent of the original amount? Explain.

Dilations

Support for Benchmarks MA.C.2.4.1, MA.C.3.4.1

EXAMPLE **Draw a dilation of quadrilateral *ABCD*. Use the origin as the center and use a scale factor of 3.**

Use the grid to find the coordinates of *ABCD*. Multiply the coordinates of each vertex of the preimage by 3 to get the coordinates of each vertex of the image.

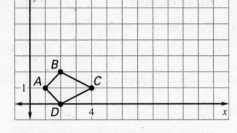

$A(1, 1) \rightarrow A'(3, 3)$

$B(2, 2) \rightarrow B'(6, 6)$

$C(4, 1) \rightarrow C'(12, 3)$

$D(2, 0) \rightarrow D'(6, 0)$

Now draw and connect the vertices of the image.

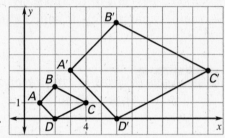

Exercises

1. Triangle *STU* is mapped onto triangle *S'T'U'* by a dilation. If $ST = 12$ and $S'T' = 2$, what is the scale factor?

   (A) $\frac{1}{6}$ (B) $\frac{1}{4}$ (C) 4   (D) 6

2. Quadrilateral *HIJK* is mapped onto quadrilateral *H'I'J'K'* by a dilation with a scale factor of 2. If $J'K' = 7$, what is *JK*?

   (F) 14   (G) 9   (H) 7   (I) 3.5

3. Jackson is using a photocopy machine to enlarge a campaign flier for class president. The size of the original flier and the desired new flier are shown on the grid. Each unit on the grid represents 1 inch. Give the dimensions of both fliers. By what scale factor does Jackson need to enlarge the original flier?

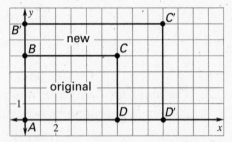

4. Terry is making a cardboard T stencil for use in painting her bedroom door. She wants to make a smaller version of the stencil that is shown on the grid. Draw a dilation of the T stencil. Use the origin as the center and use a scale factor of $\frac{1}{4}$.

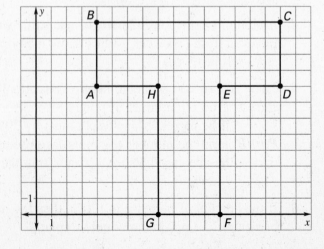

Indirect Measurement

Support for Benchmarks MA.B.2.4.1, MA.C.2.4.1

EXAMPLE **Find the value of x.**

By Theorem 9.2 you know that $\frac{KL}{KM} = \frac{KM}{JK}$.

$\frac{x}{8} = \frac{8}{6}$ **Write proportion.**

$6x = 64$ **Cross product property**

$x \approx 10.67$ **Solve for x.**

Exercises

1. Which proportion could you use to find the value of x?

(A) $\frac{8}{23} = \frac{x}{20}$ (C) $\frac{8}{x} = \frac{15}{20}$

(B) $\frac{8}{15} = \frac{x}{20}$ (D) $\frac{8}{20-x} = \frac{15}{x}$

2. Find the value of y.

(F) 3.2 (H) 12

(G) 11.25 (I) 20

3. Find the approximate value of w.

(A) 40 (C) 7.5

(B) 20 (D) 6.32

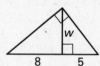

4. Two garden plots are shown at the right. The vertical sides of the garden plots are parallel. Find the value of x to the nearest tenth of a meter.

5. You want to know the height of the rim of a basketball hoop. To estimate the height of the rim, your friend uses a square to line up the bottom of the post and the back of the rim. You measure the vertical distance from the ground to your friend's eye and the distance from your friend to the post.

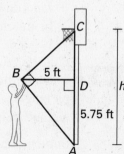

a. Explain in geometric terms why $\triangle ABD$ is similar to $\triangle BCD$.

b. Write a proportion that can be used to find CA, the height of the rim.

c. Solve the proportion to approximate the height of the rim. Show your work.

Sampling and Surveys

Support for Benchmarks MA.E.3.4.1, MA.E.3.4.2

Vocabulary

Surveys are used to gather information about a *population*. A **population** is a group of people or objects that you want information about. When it is too difficult to survey an entire population, a **sample,** or part of the population is surveyed. There are several different types of samples.

In a **simple random sample,** members are chosen using a method that gives everyone an equally likely chance of being selected. In a **systematic sample,** members are chosen using a pattern, such as selecting every other person. In a **stratified sample,** the population is first divided into groups. Then members are randomly chosen from each group. In a **convenience sample,** members are chosen because they are easily accessible. In a **self-selected sample,** members volunteer to participate.

A **biased sample** is a sample that is not representative of a population. The results of convenience and self-selected samples are likely to be biased. If the questions in a survey are phrased in such a way that they encourage certain answers, these questions are called **biased questions.**

EXAMPLE 1 The coaches in a girls' lacrosse league want to ask players about the possible use of safety goggles. They decide to ask a sample of 50 players.

a. The coaches randomly choose 5 players from each of the 10 teams in the league. This is a stratified sample because the players are separated by team and randomly chosen from each team.

b. The coaches call the first 50 players on the league phone list. This is a convenience sample because the first 50 players are easily accessible.

c. The coaches have a computer generate a list of 50 players from a database that includes all of the players in the league. This is a simple random sample because each player has an equally likely chance of being chosen.

EXAMPLE 2 The administrators at your school want to know if they should add more parking spaces in the student parking lot. Tell whether the sampling method could result in a biased sample.

Survey every 5th student on an alphabetical list of students in the school.

Solution

This method is not likely to result in a biased sample because a wide range of students will be surveyed.

Sampling and Surveys (continued)

Support for Benchmarks MA.E.3.4.1, MA.E.3.4.2

EXAMPLE 3 Tell whether the survey question may be biased.

"Do you, like most people, enjoy bike riding?"

Solution

This question may be biased because a response of "no" would imply that the respondent is not like most people. Some respondents may feel pressure to answer "yes."

Exercises

1. A town clerk wants to know whether people in the town are interested in a town water system. One household on every street is randomly selected to be surveyed. Classify the sampling method.

   (A) simple random sample   (B) stratified sample   (C) systematic sample   (D) convenience sample

2. The athletic director at a school wants to find out if students want to change the school's mascot. Which sampling method is NOT likely to result in a biased sample?

   (F) The director asks 2 randomly selected members of every sports team.

   (G) The director asks every 5th student who enters the gym.

   (H) The director leaves surveys at the front office for students to fill out.

   (I) The director asks every 10th student from a list of students in the school.

3. Which survey question may be biased?

   (A) "Which do you prefer: tasteless fish or flavorful chicken?"

   (B) "Do you listen to music regularly?"

   (C) "Which do you prefer: dogs or cats?"

   (D) "Do you use an electric toothbrush or a manual toothbrush?"

The manager of a grocery store wants to know if shoppers want self-checkout available. Tell whether the sampling method could result in a biased sample. Explain your reasoning.

4. The manager asks every 20th shopper who exits the grocery store.

5. The manager asks every 10th shopper in the "12 items or less" checkout line.

Tell whether the survey question may be biased. Explain your reasoning.

6. A supervisor asks her employees: "Do you enjoy your job?"

FCAT Spiral Review

For use after Module 7

Complete each proportion.

1. $1:4 = 12:$____

2. $2:9 = 14:$____

3. $3:5 =$ ____$:15$

4. $7:$____ $= 35:40$

5. $1:6 = 8:$____

6. $3:10 = 75:$____

7. $1:25 = 9:$____

8. $4:5 =$ ____$:100$

9. $1:36 = 4:$____

10. $8:15 = 120:$____

Identify the change as an increase or decrease and find the percent of change.

11. Original: 20, New: 30

12. Original: 20, New: 44

13. Original: 20, New: 15

14. Original: 100, New: 10

15. Original: 80, New: 10

16. Original: 50, New: 51

17. Original: 1.4, New: 1.96

18. Original: 2.2, New: 2.35

19. Original: $45.00, New: $40.50

20. Original: $45.00, New: $49.50

Determine whether the following survey questions are _biased_ or _non-biased_. If the question is biased, explain how it could be rephrased to make it non-biased.

21. Sally surveyed all of the students in her tenth grade homeroom. The students were asked to choose from a list of sports that included baseball, football, soccer, and other. Sally determined that baseball was the favorite sport of the students in her homeroom.

22. George surveyed ten of the students in his tenth grade homeroom. The students were asked to choose their favorite class at school. He determined that the favorite class of tenth graders was Biology.

23. Jake plans to buy bags of mulch to cover his garden that is a 12.5 foot by 14.5 foot rectangle. ESTIMATE the cost if each bag of mulch will cover 10 square feet and costs $2.99.

24. In a survey of car owners, 2 of every 5 owners said their car was more than five years old. On a circle graph, what angle measure would be used for the section of the graph representing this group of car owners?

25. Solve the following system of equations.
$-2x + 5y = -1$
$3x - 4y = 12$

Square Roots

Support for Benchmarks MA.A.1.4.2, MA.A.1.4.3, MA.A.1.4.4, MA.A.2.4.2, MA.A.3.4.1, MA.A.3.4.3

> If $m^2 = n$, then m is a **square root** of n. Every positive number has
> two square roots: a positive square root and a negative square root. A
> **radical sign**, $\sqrt{}$, represents a nonnegative square root. For
> example, $\sqrt{25} = 5$ and $-\sqrt{25} = -5$.
>
> You can simplify radical expressions using the following properties:
> $$\sqrt{ab} = \sqrt{a} \cdot \sqrt{b} \qquad \text{and} \qquad \sqrt{\frac{a}{b}} = \frac{\sqrt{a}}{\sqrt{b}}$$

EXAMPLE **Simplify the expression.**

 a. $\sqrt{600} = \sqrt{100 \cdot 6} = \sqrt{100} \cdot \sqrt{6} = 10\sqrt{6}$

 b. $\dfrac{\sqrt{120}}{\sqrt{5}} = \sqrt{\dfrac{120}{5}} = \sqrt{24} = \sqrt{4} \cdot \sqrt{6} = 2\sqrt{6}$

 c. $\sqrt{14} \cdot \sqrt{2} = \sqrt{14 \cdot 2} = \sqrt{28} = \sqrt{4} \cdot \sqrt{7} = 2\sqrt{7}$

 d. $\dfrac{10}{\sqrt{12}} = \dfrac{10}{2\sqrt{3}} = \dfrac{10}{2\sqrt{3}} \cdot \dfrac{\sqrt{3}}{\sqrt{3}} = \dfrac{10\sqrt{3}}{6} = \dfrac{5\sqrt{3}}{3}$

Exercises

Simplify the expression.

1. $\sqrt{250}$ **2.** $\sqrt{15} \cdot \sqrt{5}$ **3.** $\dfrac{\sqrt{60}}{\sqrt{3}}$ **4.** $\dfrac{32}{\sqrt{8}}$

5. The lengths, in inches, of the diagonals of three rectangular mirrors
are $7\sqrt{2}$, $\sqrt{181}$, and $2\sqrt{41}$. Which list gives the diagonals in order
from least to greatest?

Ⓐ $7\sqrt{2}$, $2\sqrt{41}$, $\sqrt{181}$ Ⓑ $2\sqrt{41}$, $7\sqrt{2}$, $\sqrt{181}$ Ⓒ $\sqrt{181}$, $2\sqrt{41}$, $7\sqrt{2}$ Ⓓ $\sqrt{181}$, $7\sqrt{2}$, $2\sqrt{41}$

6. Mary calculates that the length of a pool slide is $\sqrt{128}$ feet. Which of the
following is equal to this value?

Ⓕ $10\sqrt{3}$ feet Ⓖ $10\sqrt{2}$ feet Ⓗ $8\sqrt{3}$ feet Ⓘ $8\sqrt{2}$ feet

7. Using the Pythagorean Theorem, Byron finds that the length of
Ash Street is $\sqrt{5}$ miles. Which of the following numbers is
closest to $\sqrt{5}$?

Ⓐ 2 Ⓑ $2\frac{1}{4}$ Ⓒ $2\frac{1}{2}$ Ⓓ $2\frac{3}{4}$

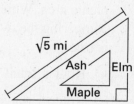

8. Sam is cutting pieces of tile, each with a length of $\sqrt{3}$ feet, from
a strip of tile that is 9 feet long. How many whole pieces of tile
can Sam cut?

Using the Pythagorean Theorem

Support for Benchmark MA.B.2.4.1

EXAMPLE A company is installing a wheelchair ramp at the entrance of their building. The length of the ramp is 246.46 centimeters and the base of the ramp is 245.67 centimeters. How far from the ground is the top of the ramp?

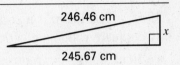

246.46 cm

245.67 cm

Solution

The height of the wheelchair ramp is a leg of a right triangle. Use the Pythagorean Theorem to find the height of the ramp.

$245.67^2 + x^2 = 246.46^2$ Pythagorean Theorem

$\quad\quad x^2 = 246.46^2 - 245.67^2$ Subtract $(245.67)^2$ from each side.

$\quad\quad x = \sqrt{246.46^2 - 245.67^2}$ Find the positive square root.

$\quad\quad x \approx 19.72$ Use a calculator to approximate.

The height of the wheelchair ramp is about 19.72 centimeters.

Exercises

1. What is the value of x in the diagram?

6 in.   8 in. x

   (A) $2\sqrt{7}$ inches   (C) 14 inches

   (B) 10 inches   (D) 48 inches

2. The hypotenuse of a right triangle has a length of 16 feet and one of the legs has a length of 4 feet. What is the length of the other leg?

   (F) $4\sqrt{15}$ feet   (G) $4\sqrt{17}$ feet   (H) 20 feet   (I) 64 feet

3. Use the diagram at the right. Tom's car is in a parking lot located on the perimeter of a rectangular park. There are two routes from the parking lot that lead Tom to the same picnic area. Which of the following statements comparing the two routes to the picnic area is true?

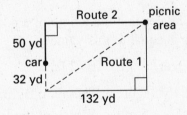

Route 2   picnic area

50 yd

car   Route 1

32 yd

132 yd

   (A) Routes 1 and 2 are the same length.   (C) Route 1 is about 10 yards shorter.

   (B) Route 1 is about 5 yards shorter.   (D) Route 1 is about 5 yards longer.

4. What is the area of the large triangle?

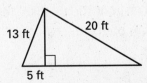

13 ft   20 ft

5 ft

   (F) $10 + 8\sqrt{2}$ square feet   (H) 68 square feet

   (G) 54 square feet   (I) 126 square feet

Angle Measures in Polygons

Support for Benchmarks MA.B.1.4.2, MA.C.1.4.1

EXAMPLE Pentagon *ABCDE* at the right is a regular pentagon.

What is the measure, in degrees, of ∠*ECD*? Explain your reasoning.

Solution

Find the measure of each interior angle of a regular pentagon.

$$\frac{1}{n} \cdot (n - 2) \cdot 180° = \frac{1}{5} \cdot (5 - 2) \cdot 180°$$ **Corollary to Theorem 11.1**

$$= 108°$$ **Simplify.**

So, the measure of ∠*CDE* is 108°.

In triangle *CDE*, $\overline{CD} \cong \overline{ED}$ because *ABCDE* is regular. This means that triangle *CDE* is an isosceles triangle. So, ∠*ECD* ≅ ∠*CED* because base angles of an isosceles triangle are congruent. Let $x° = m\angle ECD = m\angle CED$.

$$m\angle ECD + m\angle CED + m\angle CDE = 180°$$ **Triangle Sum Theorem**

$$x° + x° + 108° = 180°$$ **Substitute.**

$$x° = 36°$$ **Simplify.**

So, the measure of ∠*ECD* is 36°.

Exercises

1. What is the measure, in degrees, of ∠*PQR*?

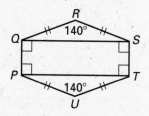

Ⓐ 20°   Ⓑ 90°   Ⓒ 100°   Ⓓ 110°

2. What is the value of *x*?

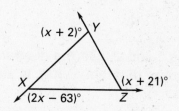

Ⓕ 10   Ⓖ 68   Ⓗ 78   Ⓘ 100

3. In quadrilateral *JKLM*, $m\angle LMJ = 4x°$, $m\angle MJK = 3x°$, $m\angle JKL = (6x - 5)°$, and $m\angle KLM = (5x + 5)°$. How many degrees does ∠*JKL* measure?

4. A convex octagon has four interior angles that each measure 120°. If the remaining interior angles are congruent, then what is the measure of each of the remaining interior angles? Explain your reasoning.

5. Polygon *ABCDEFGHIJ* is a regular decagon. Suppose that sides $\overline{AB}$ and $\overline{CD}$ are extended to intersect at *Q*. What is the measure of ∠*BQC*? Explain your reasoning.

Perimeters and Areas of Similar Figures

Support for Benchmarks MA.B.1.4.3, MA.C.2.4.1, MA.C.3.4.1

EXAMPLE A design for a park includes two triangular flower gardens. In the design shown at the right, $\triangle ABC$ is similar to $\triangle DEF$ and 1 unit equals 1 foot. If the area of the smaller garden is 5.25 square feet, then what is the area of the larger garden? Explain your reasoning.

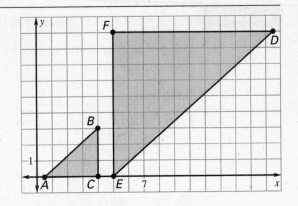

Solution

First, find the ratio of the lengths of corresponding sides. Use the diagram to determine the lengths.

$$\frac{BC}{EF} = \frac{3}{9} = \frac{1}{3}$$

Then find the area of the larger garden. Let x represent the area of the larger garden. The ratio of the areas of the smaller garden to the larger is $1^2 : 3^2$, or $1 : 9$.

$\dfrac{1}{9} = \dfrac{5.25}{x}$ **Write proportion.**

$x = 9 \cdot 5.25$ **Cross product property**

$x = 47.25$ **Multiply.**

The area of the larger garden is 47.25 square feet.

Exercises

In Exercises 1 and 2, use the diagram at the right. In the diagram, $\triangle KNL$ is similar to $\triangle MNJ$.

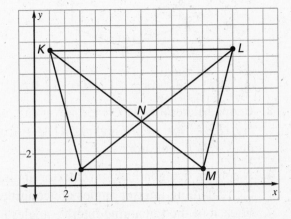

1. The area of $\triangle MNJ$ is 12 square units. How many square units is the area of $\triangle KNL$?

   (A) 12   (B) 18   (C) 24   (D) 27

2. The perimeter of $\triangle KNL$ is 27 units. How many units is the perimeter of $\triangle MNJ$?

   (F) 12   (G) 18   (H) 24   (I) 27

3. $JKLM$ and $PQRS$ are similar. $JKLM$ has a perimeter of 6 meters and an area of 63 square meters. $PQRS$ has a perimeter of x meters and an area of $x^2 + 3$ square meters. What is the value of x? Explain your reasoning.

Arc Lengths

Support for Benchmarks MA.B.1.4.1, MA.B.1.4.2

EXAMPLE The diagram at the right shows the dimensions of a city park. The park is bounded by circular arcs and line segments. What is the perimeter of the park?

15 ft
5 ft   5 ft
120°   120°
15 ft   15 ft
5 ft
120°

Solution

The park is bounded by 3 circular arcs and 3 straight sections. The 3 arcs have the same length, so find the length of one of the arcs.

$$\text{Arc length} = \frac{120°}{360°} \cdot 2\pi(5) \approx 10.5 \text{ feet}$$

Then find the sum of the lengths of the arcs and the segments.

$$\text{Perimeter} = 3(\text{length of one arc}) + 3(\text{length of one segment})$$

$$\approx 3(10.5) + 3(15)$$

$$= 76.5$$

So, the perimeter of the park is about 76.5 feet.

Exercises

In Exercises 1–3, find the perimeter of the hole on a miniature golf course. The hole is bounded by circular arcs and line segments and is shown as the shaded region.

1.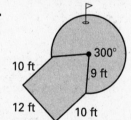

300°
10 ft   9 ft
12 ft   10 ft

2.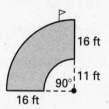

16 ft
90°   11 ft
16 ft

3.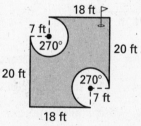

18 ft
7 ft
270°   20 ft
20 ft   270°
7 ft
18 ft

1.
(A) 32 ft   (C) 55.6 ft
(B) 47.1 ft   (D) 79.1 ft

2.
(F) 32 ft   (H) 91.7 ft
(G) 66.6 ft   (I) 116.8 ft

3.
(A) 65.9 ft   (C) 141.9 ft
(B) 76 ft   (D) 163.9 ft

In Exercises 4 and 5, use the diagram of the baseball field at the right. The field is bounded by circular arcs and line segments.

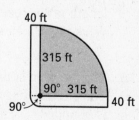

40 ft
315 ft
90°   315 ft
90°   40 ft

4. What is the perimeter of the entire region? Explain your reasoning.

5. What is the perimeter of fair territory (the shaded region)? How long will it take a player running at a constant speed of 9 feet per second to run around fair territory? Explain your reasoning.

Areas of Circles and Sectors

Support for Benchmark MA.B.1.4.1

EXAMPLE A diagram of a driveway is shown at the right. What is its area? Explain your reasoning.

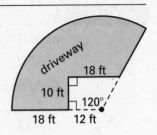

Solution

To find the area of the driveway, find the area of the sector and subtract the area of the trapezoid.

$$\text{Area} = \text{Area of sector} - \text{Area of trapezoid}$$

$$= \frac{120°}{360°} \cdot \pi(30)^2 - \frac{18 + 12}{2}(10)$$

$$= 300\pi - 150$$

$$\approx 792.5$$

The area of the driveway is about 792.5 square feet.

Exercises

In Exercises 1–3, choose the expression that could be used to find the area of the shaded region.

1.

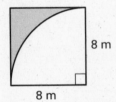

8 m

8 m

2.

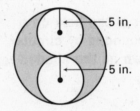

5 in.

5 in.

3.

4 ft

4 ft

(A) $16\pi - 64$ square meters

(B) $64 - 16\pi$ square meters

(C) $64 - 8\pi$ square meters

(D) $64\pi - 64$ square meters

(F) $200\pi - 50\pi$ square inches

(G) $200\pi - 25\pi$ square inches

(H) $100\pi - 50\pi$ square inches

(I) $100\pi - 25\pi$ square inches

(A) $16 + 4\pi$ square feet

(B) $8 + 8\pi$ square feet

(C) $16 + 8\pi$ square feet

(D) $16 + 16\pi$ square feet

4. The welcome mat at the right is shaped like a dog bone. It is made up of four congruent sectors and a rectangle. The length of the rectangle is 22 inches and the width is 10 inches. What is the area of the mat? Explain your reasoning.

5. The diagram at the right shows the floor plan for a new playhouse. The circular stage is in the center and the seating area (shaded region) is bounded by a regular octagon. What is the area of the shaded region? About what percent of the floor does the seating area cover?

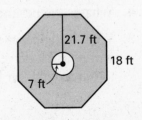

Introduction to Probability

Support for Benchmark MA.E.2.4.1

EXAMPLE What is the probability of getting at least 2 tails when tossing a
coin 3 times?

Solution

Make a tree diagram to find the outcomes.

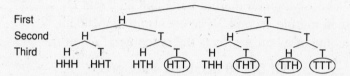

First
Second
Third

HHH HHT HTH (HTT) THH (THT) (TTH) (TTT)

Because 4 of the 8 outcomes have at least 2 tails, the probability
is $\frac{4}{8}$, or $\frac{1}{2}$.

Exercises

1. A high school has 204 freshman (99 male and 105 female),
   218 sophomores (110 male and 108 female), 212 juniors (110 male
   and 102 female), and 206 seniors (101 male and 105 female). What
   is the probability that a randomly selected student from the high
   school is male?

   (A) 0.42   (B) 0.50   (C) 0.56   (D) 0.84

2. What is the probability of getting exactly 3 heads when tossing a
   coin 4 times?

   (F) 25%   (G) 37.5%   (H) 56%   (I) 75%

3. Eric has a collection of miniature baseball bats. Each of the bats has
   a different Major League Baseball team logo on it. He has bats for 9
   of the 14 American League teams and 11 of the 16 National League
   teams. Eric randomly selects a bat from his collection. What is the
   probability that it is a bat for a National League team?

In Exercises 4 and 5, use the following information.

The spinner at the right is divided into 4 equal sections. Gabe spins the
spinner 50 times. The results are shown in the table.

Outcome	1	2	3	4
Frequency	10	12	18	10

4. What is the experimental probability of spinning a 3?

5. What is the theoretical probability of spinning a 3?

Independent and Dependent Events

Support for Benchmark MA.E.2.4.2

EXAMPLE Jamie randomly selects a marble from a bag that contains the marbles listed in the table at the right. She does not replace the first marble and randomly selects another. What is the probability that both marbles are green?

Color	Marbles
blue	2
green	4
red	3
white	1

Solution

Let event A be "choose a green marble first" and let event B be "choose a green marble second." The events are dependent because the outcome of event A affects the outcome of event B.

$$P(A) = \frac{4}{10}$$ **Of the 10 marbles, 4 are green.**

$$P(B \,|\, A) = \frac{3}{9}$$ **Of the 9 remaining marbles, 3 are green.**

$$P(A \text{ and } B) = \frac{4}{10} \cdot \frac{3}{9} = \frac{2}{15} \approx 13.3\%$$

Exercises

In Exercises 1 and 2, use the following information.

A standard deck of playing cards has 52 cards, with 13 cards in each of four suits: clubs, spades, diamonds, and hearts.

1. Marcus randomly selects one card from a full deck and does not replace it. Then he randomly selects another card. What is the probability that the first card is an ace and the second card is a jack?

   (A) $\frac{2}{2652}$ (B) $\frac{4}{663}$ (C) $\frac{8}{52}$ (D) $\frac{8}{13}$

2. Tanya randomly selects one card from a full deck and replaces the card. Then she randomly selects another card. What is the probability that the first card is a spade and the second card is a 6?

   (F) $\frac{1}{52}$ (G) $\frac{1}{51}$ (H) $\frac{3}{52}$ (I) $\frac{1}{4}$

3. The table below shows the number of students in each grade at a high school who are on one of the school's basketball teams. Suppose one player from the boys' teams and one player from the girls' teams are randomly selected. What is the probability that the boy is in the ninth grade and the girl is in the twelfth grade?

	Ninth	Tenth	Eleventh	Twelfth
Boys	⊛⊛⊛	⊛⊛⊛⊛	⊛⊛⊛◖	⊛⊛⊛⊛◖
Girls	⊛⊛◖	⊛⊛⊛⊛⊛	⊛⊛⊛⊛◖	⊛⊛⊛

Key: ⊛ represents 2 students.

Scatter Plots

Support for Benchmark MA.E.1.4.1

EXAMPLE The table shows the number of DVDs shipped (in millions) since 1998. Make a scatter plot of the data. Then sketch a line that appears to best fit the data.

Years since 1998	0	1	2	3	4
DVDs shipped (millions)	0.5	2.5	3.3	7.9	10.7

Solution

Write the data as ordered pairs. Let x be the number of years since 1998, and let y be the number of DVDs shipped (in millions).

(0, 0.5), (1, 2.5), (2, 3.3), (3, 7.9), (4, 10.7)

Plot the ordered pairs in a coordinate plane. Sketch a line that closely follows the pattern of data points.

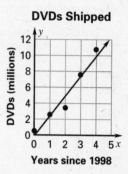

DVDs Shipped

Exercises

1. The table below shows the highway transportation energy consumption (in trillions of BTUs) by automobiles.

Year	1991	1992	1993	1994	1995	1996	1997	1998	1999	2000
Energy Consumption	8,029	8,179	8,368	8,470	8,489	8,634	8,710	8,936	9,134	9,082

Part A Make a scatter plot of the data in the table.

Part B On the scatter plot, as time increases, what happens to energy consumption?

Part C Predict what the energy consumption will be in 2005. Explain how you determined your answer.

In Exercises 2 and 3, use the scatter plot, which shows the maximum and minimum heights (in centimeters) of students in grades 7 through 12.

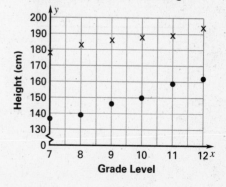

Maximum and Minimum Heights of Student's Grades 7 Through 12

2. Consider the best-fitting line for the maximum heights and the best-fitting line for the minimum heights. Which line has a greater slope? Explain.

3. What fraction of the grade levels has a maximum height that is at least 35 centimeters more than the minimum height?

(A) $\frac{1}{3}$ (B) $\frac{1}{2}$ (C) $\frac{2}{3}$ (D) $\frac{5}{6}$

FCAT Spiral Review

For use after Module 8

Simplify each radical expression.

1. $\sqrt{100}$ 2. $\sqrt{24}$ 3. $\sqrt{54}$ 4. $\sqrt{128}$

5. $\sqrt{75}$ 6. $\sqrt{80}$ 7. $\sqrt{40}$ 8. $\sqrt{72}$

9. $\sqrt{288}$ 10. $\sqrt{147}$ 11. $\sqrt{200}$ 12. $\sqrt{63}$

Complete the function tables.

	Rule: $y = 2x + 8$	
	x	**y**
13.	7	
14.	9	
15.		12
16.		5
17.	11	

	Rule: $y = -\frac{1}{2}x + 4$	
	x	**y**
18.	6	
19.		8
20.	13	
21.		20
22.		52

23. Quinn wants to enlarge an 8-inch by 10-inch photograph, using a scale of $1:3$. What will the area of the enlarged photograph be?

24. A circular dartboard has a radius of 15 inches. The inner ring has a radius of 5 inches. What is the probability that a randomly thrown dart that hits the dartboard will land inside the inner ring?

25. Matt spins a spinner that is divided into six equal sections numbered 1 through 6. Then he rolls a number cube that is numbered 1 through 6. What is the probability that both the spinner and the number cube will land on the number 4?

26. The coordinates of $\triangle KLM$ and its image, $\triangle K'L'M'$, are shown in the table. What type of transformation produced the image of $\triangle KLM$?

$\triangle KLM$	$\triangle K'L'M'$
$K(3, 2)$	$K'(-3, 2)$
$L(4, -6)$	$L'(-4, -6)$
$M(2, -1)$	$M'(-2, -1)$

Cross Sections of Solids

Support for Benchmark MA.C.2.4.2

EXAMPLE   In the diagram at the right, the shaded region is a
planar cross section of the sphere. What is the
area of the planar cross section?

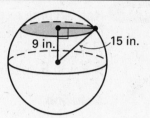

Solution

First, use the Pythagorean Theorem to find the
radius of the cross section, in inches.

$$a^2 + b^2 = c^2 \qquad \text{Pythagorean Theorem}$$
$$a^2 + (9)^2 = (15)^2 \qquad \text{Substitute.}$$
$$a^2 + 81 = 225 \qquad \text{Multiply.}$$
$$a^2 = 144 \qquad \text{Subtract 81 from each side.}$$
$$a = 12 \qquad \text{Find the positive square root.}$$

Then find the area of the circular cross section.

$$A = \pi r^2 = \pi \cdot (12)^2 = 144\pi \approx 452.2 \text{ square inches}$$

Exercises

1. Which figure describes the planar cross section of the
   square pyramid at the right?

   (A) rectangle   (C) trapezoid

   (B) square   (D) triangle

2. Which figure is a possible planar cross section of a circular cone?

   (F) pentagon   (G) rectangle   (H) square   (I) triangle

3. A sphere has a radius of 7 meters. What is the area of a planar cross
   section that passes through the center of the sphere?

   (A) 7π square meters   (C) 49π square meters

   (B) 14π square meters   (D) 70π square meters

4. A log has been milled so that it is a cylinder with a
   radius of 2 feet and a length of 18 feet. The log is cut
   through the middle as shown at the right. What is the
   area of the planar cross section?

   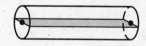

   (F) 36 square feet   (G) 72 square feet   (H) 81 square feet   (I) 72π square feet

5. A rectangular sheet cake is cut along a diagonal as shown
   at the right. What is the area of the planar cross section?

   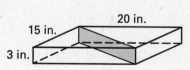

   (A) 25 square inches   (C) 60 square inches

   (B) 48 square inches   (D) 75 square inches

Surface Area

Support for Benchmark MA.B.1.4.1

EXAMPLE Rob is going to paint the outer surfaces of the CD storage unit shown at the right, which is a rectangular prism. What is the area of the surface that will be painted?

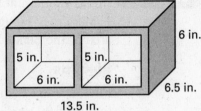

Solution

To find the area of the outer surfaces, find the surface area of the rectagular prism and subtract the area of the openings.

Area of outer surfaces = Surface area of prism − Area of openings
$$= 2B + Ph - 2(lw)$$
$$= 2(13.5 \cdot 6.5) + (2 \cdot 13.5 + 2 \cdot 6.5)(6) - 2(5 \cdot 6)$$
$$= 2(87.75) + 40(6) - 2(30)$$
$$= 355.5$$

The area that will be painted is 355.5 square inches.

Exercises

1. The figure below is composed of two cones. Which expression can be used to find its surface area?

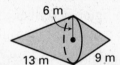

(A) $54\pi + 25\pi$ square meters

(B) $78\pi + 25\pi$ square meters

(C) $78\pi + 54\pi$ square meters

(D) $78\pi + 54\pi + 36\pi$ square meters

In Exercises 2 and 3, find the surface area of the structure to the nearest square foot. Use $\pi \approx 3.14$. Do not include the area of the structure that rests on the ground, but do include the area of the door.

2. The figure shown at the right is composed of a cylinder and a cone.

3. The greenhouse shown at the right is composed of a rectangular prism and half of a cylinder.

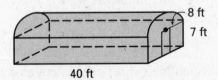

4. The figure at the right is composed of a regular pyramid with a square base and a cube. The surface area of the figure is 240 square meters. What is the value of x? Explain your reasoning.

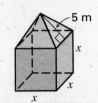

Volume

Support for Benchmark MA.B.1.4.1

EXAMPLE The candleholder at the right is a rectangular
prism with a cylindrical opening. What is its volume?

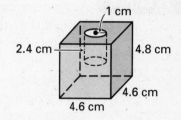

1 cm

2.4 cm   4.8 cm

4.6 cm

4.6 cm

Solution

To find the volume, subtract the volume of the
cylinder from the volume of the rectangular prism.

Volume = Volume of prism − Volume of cylinder

$$= Bh - \pi r^2 h$$
$$= 4.6 \cdot 4.6 \cdot 4.8 - \pi \cdot 1^2 \cdot 2.4$$
$$\approx 94$$

The volume of the candleholder is about 94 cubic centimeters.

Exercises

1. The diagram at the right shows an aquarium with a
   walkway. The aquarium is a rectangular prism and the
   walkway is half of a cylinder. Which expression can be
   used to find the volume of the aquarium, not including the
   walkway?

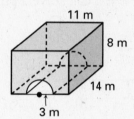

11 m

8 m

14 m

3 m

   (A) $1,232 - 126\pi$ cubic meters

   (B) $1,232 - 63\pi$ cubic meters

   (C) $1,232 - 9\pi$ cubic meters

   (D) $1,232 + 9\pi$ cubic meters

**In Exercises 2–4, find the volume of the solid to the nearest cubic
foot. Use $\pi \approx 3.14$.**

2.   3.   4.

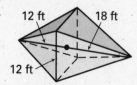

12 ft   18 ft

12 ft

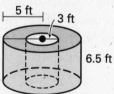

5 ft   3 ft

6.5 ft

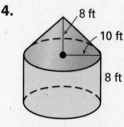

8 ft

10 ft

8 ft

5. The directions on a box of cake mix state that the cake
   should be baked in a rectangular pan with a length of
   13 inches, a width of 9 inches, and a height of 2 inches.
   Can the two cylindrical pans at the right be used instead of
   the rectangular pan? Explain your reasoning.

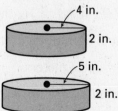

4 in.

2 in.

5 in.

2 in.

Similar Solids

Support for Benchmarks MA.B.1.4.3, MA.C.2.4.1, MA.D.1.4.2

EXAMPLE A company that manufactures hair care products decides to make
travel-sized versions of their existing products. They want to use a
label that covers the bottle without covering the top and bottom.
They want to use one fourth as much paper to make the label for the
travel-sized versions. If the travel-sized shampoo bottle is similar
to the existing shampoo bottle with the dimensions shown at the
right, then what is the height of the travel-sized shampoo bottle?

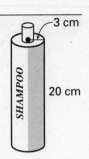

Solution

The scale factor of the cylinders is the ratio of their corresponding linear measures.
Let x represent the height of the travel-sized bottle. Then the scale

factor is $\frac{x}{20}$. By the Similar Solids Theorem, the ratio of their corresponding

lateral areas is $\frac{x^2}{20^2}$. Because the ratio of their lateral areas is also equal to $\frac{1}{4}$,

you can solve a proportion to find the height of the travel-sized bottle.

$\frac{1}{4} = \frac{x^2}{20^2}$ Write proportion.

$400 = 4x^2$ Cross products property

$100 = x^2$ Divide each side by 4.

$10 = x$ Take the positive root of each side.

The height of the travel-sized bottle is 10 centimeters.

Exercises

1. What is the scale factor of the two similar prisms?

   (A) 1 : 3   (C) 3 : 5

   (B) 1 : 2   (D) 3 : 4

$V = 125 \text{ ft}^3$

$V = 27 \text{ ft}^3$

2. Anne just made a cylindrical pillow. She decides to make another
cylindrical pillow by doubling the dimensions of her first pillow.
If her first pillow required 340 cubic inches of polyester fiber
stuffing, then how how many cubic inches of stuffing will she
need for her larger pillow?

3. In the diagram at the right, pyramids *ABCDE* and *FGHJE* are
similar. The volume of *ABCDE* is 8 times as large as the volume of
FGHJE. If *AB* = 16, then what is *FG*? Explain your reasoning.

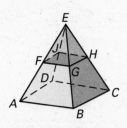

4. What is the volume of the larger of the two similiar cones?

   (F) 3π cubic meters

   (G) 9π cubic meters

   (H) 27π cubic meters

   (I) 81π cubic meters

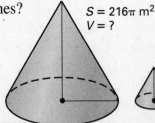

$S = 216\pi \text{ m}^2$
$V = ?$

$S = 24\pi \text{ m}^2$
$V = 3\pi \text{ m}^3$

FCAT Spiral Review

For use after Module 9

Find the surface area and volume of each solid. Use 3.14 for π.

1.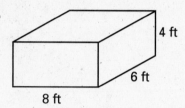
4 ft
6 ft
8 ft

2.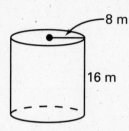
8 m
16 m

3.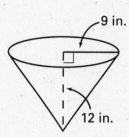
9 in.
12 in.

Write each number in standard form.

4. 4.45×10^7

5. 3.07×10^{-4}

6. 1.1106×10^3

Match each equation with an equation of a perpendicular line.

7. $y = -2x + 3$

8. $-y = \frac{1}{2}x + \frac{1}{3}$

9. $y = 2x - 3$

10. $2y = x - \frac{2}{3}$

A. $y = -\frac{1}{2}x - \frac{1}{3}$

B. $y = \frac{1}{2}x - 3$

C. $\frac{1}{2}y = x + \frac{3}{2}$

D. $-y = 2x - \frac{1}{3}$

11. A homing pigeon is released 24 miles east and 10 miles north of its home. If the pigeon flies straight to its home at a constant speed of 20 miles per hour, in how many **minutes** will the pigeon reach its home?

12. The table below shows the number of CDs bought at a music store and the total cost of the CDs. Make a scatter plot and approximate the best-fitting line for the data. Then use your model to estimate the total cost of buying 7 CDs.

CDs	1	2	3	4	5	6	8	9
Total cost	$11.99	$23.98	$32.97	$46.96	$66.95	$78.94	$105.92	$118.91

The test scores of three students are shown in the Venn diagram at the right.

13. What is Antoine's highest test score?

14. How many test scores do Antoine and Sarah have in common?

15. Which student did NOT get a score of 76?

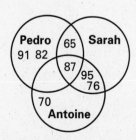

MODULE 1 Mid-Module Quiz

For use after Lesson 1.4

1. Jamie wrote out the following sequence of numbers on a sheet of paper. What number would be next in the sequence of numbers? 5, 11, 18, 26. . .

2. Matt drew the cube shown below and labeled the vertices as shown. Which point is coplanar with points A, C, and E?

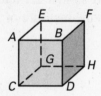

Ⓐ B

Ⓑ G

Ⓒ D

Ⓓ H

3. M is the midpoint of $\overline{LN}$. If $LM = 5x - 10$ and $MN = 2x + 2$, what is LN?

Ⓕ 4

Ⓖ 10

Ⓗ 15

Ⓘ 20

4. The map below shows the coordinates of 5 different cities. Use the Distance Formula to find the distance between city A and city B.

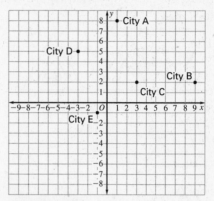

5. The diagram below shows a clock face reading 1:40. Classify the angle made by the clock's hands.

Ⓐ acute

Ⓑ right

Ⓒ obtuse

Ⓓ straight

MULTIPLE CHOICE   In Exercises 1–5, fill in the bubble for the correct answer.

1. Ted drew the figures below. If he were to continue the pattern, which figure would he draw next?

Ⓐ

Ⓑ

Ⓒ

Ⓓ

2. Which statement best describes the figure below?

Ⓕ three lines that intersect at a point and all lie in the same plane

Ⓖ three lines that intersect at a point but do not all lie in the same plane

Ⓗ three points that are coplanar but not collinear

Ⓘ three planes that intersect in a line

3. Mark drew the figure shown below on the coordinate plane. Using the Distance Formula, what is the distance between point *A* and point *B*?

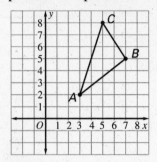

Ⓐ 2.24

Ⓑ 5

Ⓒ 12.21

Ⓓ 25

4. When a billiards ball bounces off of the side rail, it bounces off so that ∠1 and ∠2 are congruent. What is the measure of ∠4?

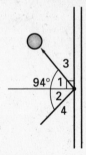

Ⓕ 86°

Ⓖ 57°

Ⓗ 43°

Ⓘ 4°

5. A rectangular photograph that is 12 inches wide and 16 inches long is surrounded by a frame that is 4 inches wide on each side. What is the perimeter of the frame?

Ⓐ 88 inches

Ⓑ 96 inches

Ⓒ 480 inches

Ⓓ 880 inches

Name _____   Date _____

Module Test

For use after Module 1

GRIDDED RESPONSE   In Exercises 6–13, grid the correct answer on the separate gridding sheet.

6. Larry wrote the following pattern of numbers. What number would come next in the sequence?

   3, 11, 19, 27, 35, . . .

7. If Michael were to put his school at (0, 0) on a coordinate plane, his house would be located at (6, 8). If each unit is equal to $\frac{1}{10}$ of a mile, how many miles away from the school is Michael's house?

8. Frank drew a line segment in a coordinate plane with endpoints at (3, 8) and (7, 2). What is the x-coordinate of the midpoint of the line segment?

9. $\angle ABC$ is bisected by $\overrightarrow{BD}$. If the measure of $\angle ABC$ is 136°, then what is the measure, in degrees, of $\angle ABD$?

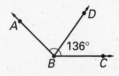

10. $\angle WXY$ is bisected by $\overrightarrow{XZ}$. What is the value of x if $m\angle WXZ = (x + 35)°$ and $m\angle YXZ = (4x + 5)°$?

11. Rachel drew the figure below. If $m\angle 3 = 72°$, then $m\angle 4$ is equal to how many degrees?

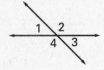

12. $\angle A$ and $\angle B$ are complementary angles. If $m\angle A = (3x + 6)°$ and $m\angle B = (6x + 12)°$, what is $m\angle A$ in degrees?

13. $\angle A$ and $\angle B$ are supplementary angles. If $m\angle A = (5x + 42)°$ and $m\angle B = (3x + 18)°$, what is $m\angle B$ in degrees?

SHORT RESPONSE   In Exercise 14, write your answer on a separate piece of paper.

14. A triangle has an area of 132 square feet and a base of 24 feet. What is the height of the triangle? Explain how you arrived at your answer.

EXTENDED RESPONSE   In Exercise 15, answer all parts on a separate piece of paper.

15. The rim of a bicycle wheel has a radius of 16 inches.

   Part A Suppose you needed to wrap the outside of the rim with rim tape to keep the spokes from poking into the tire's inner tube. Find the length of the rim tape needed by finding the circumference of the rim. (Use $\pi \approx 3.14$.)

   Part B Suppose that the circumference of the outside of the tire put onto the rim is 24 inches greater than the circumference of the rim. Find the radius of the outside of the tire. Round your answer to the nearest hundredth of an inch. Show your work.

   Part C Use your result from part (b) to find how high the tire is off of the edge of the rim.

1. Janet wrote the statement "If all of the data values are between 1 and 10, then the mean is between 1 and 10". Decide which of the following are true.
   I. The statement is false.
   II. The converse of the statement is false.
   III. The inverse of the statement is false.
   (A) I only
   (B) II only
   (C) II and III
   (D) I, II, and III

2. Which statement is the converse of the statement below?
   If x is 7, then y is 4.
   (F) If x is not 7, then y is not 4.
   (G) If y is 4, then x is 7.
   (H) If y is not 4, then x is not 7.
   (I) If x is 7, then y is not 4.

3. Which statement represents $\sim q \rightarrow \sim p$?
   p: $\angle 1$ measures $90°$.
   q: $\angle 1$ is a right angle.
   (A) If $\angle 1$ measures $90°$, then $\angle 1$ is a right angle.
   (B) If $\angle 1$ does not measure $90°$, then $\angle 1$ is not a right angle.
   (C) If $\angle 1$ is a right angle, then $\angle 1$ measures $90°$.
   (D) If $\angle 1$ is not a right angle, then $\angle 1$ does not measure $90°$.

4. The two statements below are true. What is the value of z?
   If $3x - 9 = 15$, then $y = x$.
   If $y = x$, then $z + y = 11$.

5. The two statements below are true. What is the measure of $\angle 6$ in degrees?
   If $m\angle 6 = (2x + 1)°$, then $m\angle 3 = (3x - 24)°$.
   If $m\angle 3 = (3x - 24)°$, then $m\angle 3 = m\angle 6$.

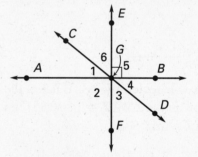

MULTIPLE CHOICE In Exercises 1–6, fill in the bubble for the correct answer.

1. Lars wrote the statement "If the least and greatest values of a data set are 25 and 100, then the mean, median, and mode are between 25 and 100." Which of the following are true?

   I. The statement is true.

   II. The contrapositive of the statement is true.

   III. The inverse of the statement is false.

   (A) I only

   (B) II only

   (C) I and III

   (D) I, II, and III

2. Use the following true statements to determine which statement is NOT true.
   If $m\angle 1 = 30°$, then $m\angle 2 = 45°$.
   If $m\angle 2 = 45°$, then $m\angle 3 = 135°$.

   (F) If $m\angle 3 \neq 135°$, then $m\angle 2 \neq 45°$.

   (G) If $m\angle 1 = 30°$, then $m\angle 3 = 135°$.

   (H) If $m\angle 2 = 45°$, then $m\angle 3 = 135°$.

   (I) If $m\angle 2 \neq 45°$, then $m\angle 1 = 30°$.

3. Allen wrote the following statement: If $AB = BC$, then $AB + 4 = BC + 4$. Which property could be used as a reason why this statement is true?

   (A) Subtraction Property of Equality

   (B) Addition Property of Equality

   (C) Symmetric Property of Equality

   (D) Transitive Property of Equality

4. In $WXYZ$, $\overline{WX} \cong \overline{YZ}$ and $WX = 78$. What is the value of a?

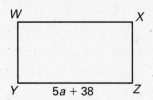

   (F) 4

   (G) 8

   (H) 32

   (I) 38

5. Emily drew the figure below. $\overline{AB}$ and $\overline{EF}$ are perpendicular. If $m\angle 2 = 75°$, then what is $m\angle 5$?

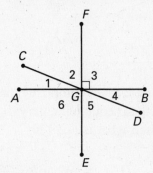

   (A) 15°

   (B) 35°

   (C) 75°

   (D) 105°

6. If $\angle 7$ and $\angle 8$ form a linear pair and $m\angle 7 = 88°$, then what is $m\angle 8$?

   (F) 180°

   (G) 92°

   (H) 88°

   (I) 2°

GRIDDED RESPONSE In Exercises 7–14, grid the correct answer on the separate gridding sheet.

7. If $m\angle 1 = 25°$ and $\angle 1$ and $\angle 2$ are supplementary, what is $m\angle 2$ in degrees?

8. What value of x makes $2(x - 13) + 4 = 24$ a true statement?

9. In the figure below, $\overline{AB}$ and $\overline{EF}$ are perpendicular. If $m\angle 4 = 20°$, what is $m\angle 2$, in degrees?

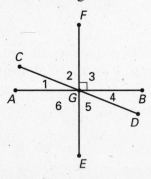

10. Suppose $\angle 7$ and $\angle 8$ are complementary and $\angle 8$ and $\angle 9$ are complementary. If $m\angle 7 = 43°$, then what is $m\angle 9$ in degrees?

11. In the diagram, $AD = 24$. What is BC?

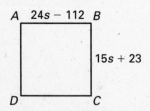

12. In the diagram above, what is CD?

13. Point C is the midpoint of $\overline{AB}$. If $AB = 58$, what is the value of x?

$$\overset{8x-3}{\underset{A \qquad\qquad C}{\rule{3cm}{0.4pt}}}\overset{5x+9}{\underset{\qquad\qquad B}{\rule{3cm}{0.4pt}}}$$

14. In $ABCD$, $\overline{AB} \cong \overline{DC}$ and $\overline{BC} \cong \overline{DC}$. What is the value of s?

$$
\begin{array}{l}
A \quad 24s - 112 \quad B \\
\Box \\
\qquad\qquad 15s + 23 \\
D \qquad\qquad C
\end{array}
$$

SHORT RESPONSE In Exercise 15, write your answer on a separate piece of paper.

15. In the diagram, $\angle ABC$ and $\angle CDB$ are supplementary. Explain why $\angle CBD \cong \angle CDB$.

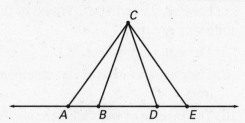

EXTENDED RESPONSE In Exercise 16, answer all parts on a separate piece of paper.

16. *Part A* Draw two lines that intersect at a single point, and label all angles so that the following are true: $\angle 1$ and $\angle 3$ are adjacent angles and $\angle 2$ and $\angle 4$ are adjacent angles.

   Part B State all of the pairs of congruent angles.

   Part C Suppose $m\angle 1 = 35°$. Find the measures of the remaining angles.

Name _____ Date _____

Mid-Module Quiz

For use after Lesson 3.4

1. Which of the following describes the lines that run through $\overline{AB}$ and $\overline{CG}$?

   (A) coplanar
   (B) parallel
   (C) skew
   (D) intersecting

Use the figure below for Exercises 2 and 3.

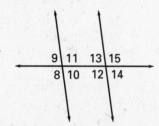

2. What kind of angles are $\angle 9$ and $\angle 13$?

   (F) corresponding
   (G) alternate interior
   (H) alternate exterior
   (I) consecutive interior

3. What kind of angles are $\angle 8$ and $\angle 15$?

   (A) corresponding
   (B) alternate interior
   (C) alternate exterior
   (D) consecutive interior

4. Which of the following is true if $a \perp b$?

   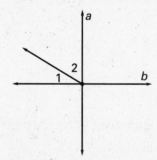

   (F) $m\angle 1 + m\angle 2 = 90°$
   (G) $m\angle 1 + m\angle 2 > 90°$
   (H) $m\angle 1 + m\angle 2 < 90°$
   (I) $m\angle 1 + m\angle 2 = 180°$

5. Lines a and b are parallel. Line c is a transversal. Find the value of x.

   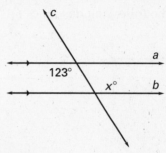

   (A) 57°
   (B) 90°
   (C) 123°
   (D) 180°

6. Lines a and b are parallel. Line c is a transversal. Find the value of x.

   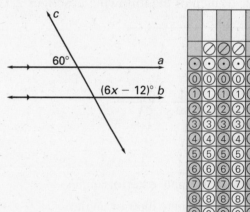

7. What value of x would make lines l_1 and l_2 parallel?

   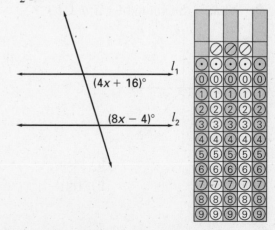

Module Test

For use after Module 3

MULTIPLE CHOICE   In Exercises 1–7, fill in the bubble for the correct answer.

1. Which of the following describes $\overleftrightarrow{DC}$ and $\overleftrightarrow{HG}$?

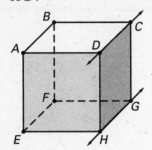

  (A) coplanar
  (B) intersecting
  (C) parallel
  (D) skew

2. Which of the following describes $\angle 11$ and $\angle 12$?

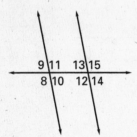

  (F) alternate exterior angles
  (G) alternate interior angles
  (H) consecutive interior angles
  (I) corresponding angles

3. What is the value of x if $a \perp b$?

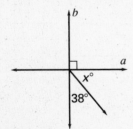

  (A) 38   (C) 90
  (B) 52   (D) 180

4. Lines a and b are parallel and line c is a transversal. What is the value of x?

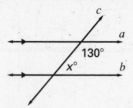

  (F) 50
  (G) 90
  (H) 130
  (I) 180

5. Jill drew the figure below. Which sets of lines are parallel?

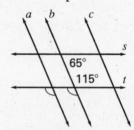

  (A) s and t
  (B) s and t, a and b
  (C) s and t, a and b and c
  (D) no lines are parallel

6. Which of the following is an equation of a line parallel to $y + 8 = 4x$?

  (F) $y - 2 = \frac{1}{4}x$
  (G) $y + 8 = \frac{1}{4}x$
  (H) $y + 4 = 8x$
  (I) $y - 2 = 4x$

7. Which of the following is an equation of a line perpendicular to $y + 3 = \frac{1}{2}x$?

  (A) $y - 5 = -2x$
  (B) $y + 8 = 2x$
  (C) $y + 3 = -\frac{1}{2}x$
  (D) $y - 7 = 4x$

GRIDDED RESPONSE   In Exercises 8–12, grid the correct answer on the separate gridding sheet.

8. Laura drew the figure below. What is the value of x in degrees?

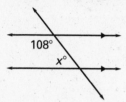

108°

x°

9. What value of x would make lines a and b parallel?

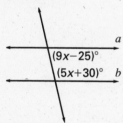

a

$(9x-25)°$

$(5x+30)°$ b

10. What value of x would make lines b and c parallel?

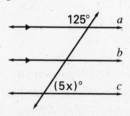

125°   a

b

$(5x)°$ c

11. What is the slope of the line that passes through the points (0, 4) and (5, 5)?

12. A ramp has a height of 8 feet and a length of 32 feet. What is the slope of the ramp?

SHORT RESPONSE   In Exercise 13, write your answer on a separate piece of paper.

13. Find the slope of $\overleftrightarrow{AC}$ and $\overleftrightarrow{BD}$. Decide whether $\overleftrightarrow{AC}$ is perpendicular to $\overleftrightarrow{BD}$.

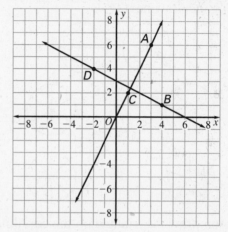

EXTENDED RESPONSE   In Exercise 14, answer all parts on a separate piece of paper.

14. Use the diagram below.

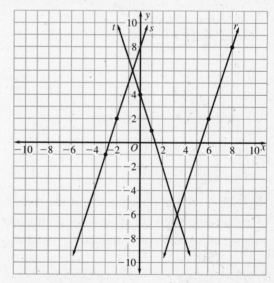

Part A Find the slope of each of the lines shown.

Part B Is r parallel to s? How do you know?

Part C Is t perpendicular to s? How do you know?

Name _____ Date _____

Cumulative Test

For use after Modules 1-3

MULTIPLE CHOICE   In Exercises 1–15, fill in the bubble for the correct answer.

1. Amy drew the figures shown below. If she continues the pattern, which figure will she draw next?

(A)

(C)

(B)

(D)

2. Jason drew the triangle on the coordinate plane shown below. Using the Distance Formula, what is the distance between point A and point B?

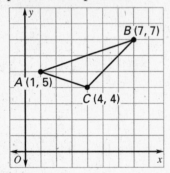

(F) 40   (H) $\sqrt{36}$

(G) $\sqrt{40}$ (I) 4

3. What are the coordinates of the midpoint of a line segment whose endpoints are given by the coordinates $(7, -4)$ and $(-5, 6)$?

(A) $(5, -6)$ (C) $(2, 0)$

(B) $(1, 1)$ (D) $(-1, -1)$

4. The diagram below shows the angles formed by a cue ball bouncing off the rail of a billiards table. If $\angle 1$ and $\angle 4$ are congruent, what is the measure of $\angle 3$?

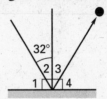

(F) $22°$ (H) $58°$

(G) $32°$ (I) $68°$

5. In the diagram below, what are the values of x and y?

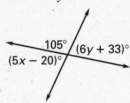

(A) $x = 19; y = 7$

(B) $x = 27; y = 5$

(C) $x = 7; y = 19$

(D) $x = 95; y = 15$

6. A rectangular photograph measuring 10 inches by 15 inches is surrounded by a frame that is 3 inches wide. What is the area of the photograph and frame combined?

(F) 50 square inches

(G) 74 square inches

(H) 300 square inches

(I) 336 square inches

Cumulative Test

For use after Modules 1-3

7. Which of the following properties makes the statement below **true**?

If $x = y$, then $y = x$.

- (A) Reflexive Property
- (B) Substitution Property
- (C) Symmetric Property
- (D) Transitive Property

8. Using the Law of Syllogism, which of the following conditional statements follows the true statements below?

If I practice my geometry problems, then I will understand geometry better.
If I undertstand geometry better, then I will get a good grade on my test.

- (F) If I get a good grade on my test, then I will practice my geometry problems.
- (G) If I understand geometry better, then I will practice my geometry problems.
- (H) If I get a good grade on my test, then I will understand geometry better.
- (I) If I practice my geometry problems, then I will get a good grade on my test.

9. In rectangle $WXYZ$, $\overline{WX} \cong \overline{YZ}$ and $\overline{WY} \cong \overline{XZ}$. What is the value of a?

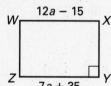

- (A) 5
- (B) 10
- (C) 12
- (D) 50

10. In the diagram below, lines AB and EF are perpendicular. If $m\angle 2 = 67°$, then what is the measure of $\angle 3$?

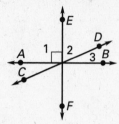

- (F) 23°
- (H) 90°
- (G) 33°
- (I) 113°

11. Which of the following terms best describes the relationship between $\overline{AH}$ and $\overline{HC}$ in the figure below?

- (A) coplanar
- (C) perpendicular
- (B) parallel
- (D) skew

12. Which of the following terms best describes $\angle 2$ and $\angle 8$ in the figure below?

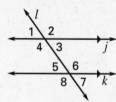

- (F) alternate exterior
- (G) alternate interior
- (H) consecutive exterior
- (I) consecutive interior

13. What is the value of x if $\overline{AC} \perp \overline{DF}$?

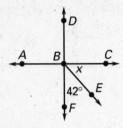

- (A) $42°$
- (B) $48°$
- (C) $90°$
- (D) $132°$

14. In the diagram below, lines a and b are parallel, and line c is a transversal. What is the value of x?

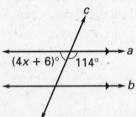

- (F) 15
- (G) 21
- (H) 27
- (I) 46

15. Which of the following is an equation of a line that is perpendicular to the line with the equation $y - 7 = 4x$?

- (A) $y = -\frac{1}{4}x + 7$
- (B) $y = \frac{1}{4}x - 7$
- (C) $y = -4x + 7$
- (D) $y = 4x - 7$

GRIDDED RESPONSE In Exercises 16–29, grid the correct answer on the separate gridding sheet.

16. If the pattern of numbers shown below continues, what will be the next number in the sequence?

3, 6, 18, 72, 360…

17. On a coordinate grid, each unit is equal to $\frac{1}{10}$ mile. Joseph plotted the location of his school at $(1, 1)$ and the location of his house at $(9, 7)$ on the plane. Using the Distance Formula, how many miles does Joseph live from his school?

18. What is the y-coordinate of the midpoint of the line segment with endpoints at $(-2, 4)$ and $(7, 0)$?

19. In the diagram below, $\overrightarrow{BD}$ bisects $\angle ABC$. What is the value of x?

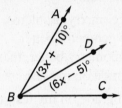

20. In the diagram below, if $m\angle 3 = 65°$, then what is the measure of $\angle 4$, in degrees?

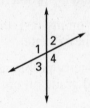

21. In the diagram below, $\angle ABC$ and $\angle CBD$ are complementary angles. What is the measure of $\angle ABC$, in degrees?

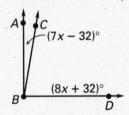

22. In the diagram below, $\angle ABC$ and $\angle CBD$ are supplementary angles. What is the measure of $\angle CBD$, in degrees?

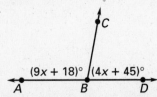

23. If $EF + GH = 47$ units and $EF = 11$ units, then how many units long is GH?

24. If $m\angle X = 53°$, then what is the value, in degrees, of $24° + m\angle X$?

25. In the diagram below, $\overline{AB} \cong \overline{BC}$ and $\overline{CD} \cong \overline{BC}$. What is the value of x?

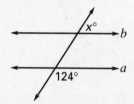

26. In the diagram below, lines a and b are parallel and line c is a transversal. What is the value of x?

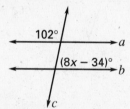

27. In the diagram below, lines a and b are parallel and line c is a transversal. What is the value of x?

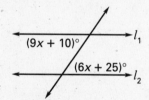

28. What value of x makes $l_1 \parallel l_2$?

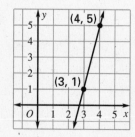

29. What is the slope of the line passing through the labeled points on the coordinate plane?

SHORT RESPONSE In Exercises 30–31, write your answer on a separate piece of paper.

30. Rewrite the biconditional statement below as a conditional statement and its converse.

An angle is a right angle if and only if it has a measure of 90°.

31. On the coordinate plane below, are line AC and line BD parallel? Justify your answer.

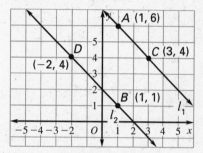

EXTENDED RESPONSE In Exercise 32, write your answer to all parts on a separate piece of paper.

32. The inside rim of Jenna's cylindrical drum has a radius of 18 inches. The circumference of the outside rim of the drum is 3.14 inches longer than the circumference of the inside rim.

Part A Jenna needs to wrap the inside rim of the drum with tape to keep it from ringing. How many inches of tape will she need to wrap around the entire inside rim of the drum?

Part B Use your result from Part A to find how many inches thick the drum is—from its inside rim to its outside rim. Explain how you found your answer.

Name _____   Date _____

MODULE 4 — Mid-Module Quiz

For use after Lesson 4.4

1. The lengths of the two legs of an isosceles triangle are represented by the expressions $4x - 15$ and $2x - 2$. The length of the base is 5 cm and the perimeter of the triangle is 27 cm. What is the value of x?

2. The sides of a scalene triangle are represented by x, $x - 1$, and $x + 1$. The perimeter of the triangle is 18 inches. What are the lengths of the 3 sides in inches?

   Ⓐ 4, 6, 7   Ⓒ 5, 6, 8
   Ⓑ 5, 6, 7   Ⓓ 6, 7, 8

3. Given $\angle A \cong \angle D$ and $\angle B \cong \angle E$, what is the value of x?

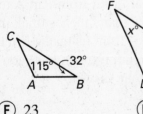

   Ⓕ 23   Ⓗ 54
   Ⓖ 33   Ⓘ 147

4. In scalene triangles ABC and MNO, $\overline{AB} \cong \overline{NO}$, $\overline{BC} \cong \overline{OM}$, and $\overline{CA} \cong \overline{MN}$. Which angle is congruent to $\angle C$?

   Ⓐ $\angle M$
   Ⓑ $\angle N$
   Ⓒ $\angle O$
   Ⓓ cannot be determined

5. In equilateral triangle RST, a segment is drawn from point R to the midpoint A of the base, $\overline{ST}$. Which of the statements below is NOT true?

   Ⓕ $\overline{RS} \cong \overline{RT}$
   Ⓖ $\overline{SA} \cong \overline{RA}$
   Ⓗ $\overline{TA} \cong \overline{SA}$
   Ⓘ $\triangle RAS \cong \triangle RAT$

6. Which postulate or theorem can be used to prove that triangle ABC is congruent to triangle CDA?

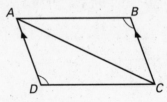

   Ⓐ SSS
   Ⓑ SAS
   Ⓒ ASA
   Ⓓ AAS

MULTIPLE CHOICE   In Exercises 1–7, fill in the bubble for the correct answer.

1. The lengths of the two legs of an isosceles triangle are represented by the expressions $(8x - 32)$ cm and $(x + 24)$ cm. The perimeter of the triangle is 90 cm. Find the length of the base of the triangle.

   (A) 8 cm

   (B) 26 cm

   (C) 32 cm

   (D) 64 cm

2. The measures of the interior angles of a scalene triangle are shown below. What is the value of x?

   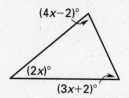

   (F) 2

   (G) 10

   (H) 20

   (I) 180

3. Given $\angle A \cong \angle D$ and $\angle B \cong \angle E$, find the value of x.

   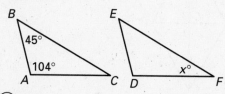

   (A) 31

   (B) 54

   (C) 76

   (D) 135

4. In $\triangle FGH$ and $\triangle XYZ$, $\overline{FG} \cong \overline{XY}$, $\overline{GH} \cong \overline{YZ}$, and $\overline{HF} \cong \overline{ZX}$. Which angle is congruent to $\angle G$?

   (F) $\angle X$

   (G) $\angle Y$

   (H) $\angle Z$

   (I) cannot be determined

5. Find the value of x.

   (A) 15

   (B) 21

   (C) 84

   (D) 105

   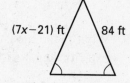

6. In quadrilateral $ABCD$, $\overline{BC} \parallel \overline{AD}$ and $\overline{BC} \cong \overline{AD}$. Which postulate or theorem can be used to show $\triangle ABD \cong \triangle CDB$?

   (F) SSS Congruence Postulate

   (G) ASA Congruence Postulate

   (H) AAS Congruence Theorem

   (I) SAS Congruence Postulate

7. Which of the algebraic expressions below can be used to find the value of x?

   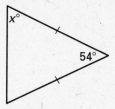

   (A) $\dfrac{180}{2} - 54$

   (B) $\dfrac{180 - 54}{2}$

   (C) $180 - \dfrac{54}{2}$

   (D) $180 - 54$

Module Test

For use after Module 4

GRIDDED RESPONSE In Exercises 8–14, grid the correct answer on the separate gridding sheet.

8. What is the measure of ∠1?

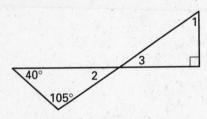

9. What is the measure, in degrees, of the exterior angle shown?

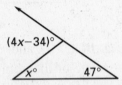

10. What is the value of *x* that makes *r* ∥ *s*?

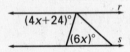

11. Given ∠*K* ≅ ∠*D* and ∠*J* ≅ ∠*C*, what is the value of *s* in degrees?

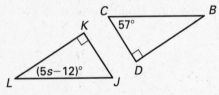

12. What is the value of *y*?

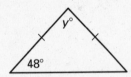

13. What is the value of *x*?

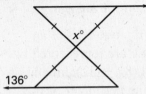

14. What is the value of *x*?

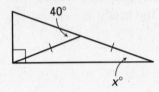

SHORT RESPONSE In Exercise 15, write your answer on a separate piece of paper.

15. Place a 5-unit by 8-unit rectangle in a coordinate plane and find the length of a diagonal drawn from opposite corners. Explain how you found the length.

EXTENDED RESPONSE In Exercise 16, answer all parts on a separate piece of paper.

16. In the diagram shown, △*ABD* and △*CBD* are congruent isosceles triangles.

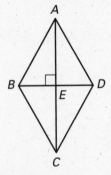

Part A Explain why △*ABC* is isosceles.
Part B Explain why ∠*BAE* ≅ ∠*BCE*.
Part C Explain why △*ABE* ≅ △*CBE*.

Name _____   Date _____

Mid-Module Quiz

For use after Lesson 6.3

1. Which statement about the diagram below is NOT true?

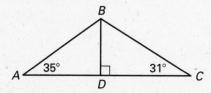

- (A) $BC > BA$
- (B) $m\angle DAB > m\angle DCB$
- (C) $m\angle CBD > m\angle ABD$
- (D) $AD > CD$

2. The diagram shows parallelogram $ABCD$. What is the value of x?

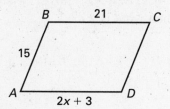

- (F) 6
- (G) 9
- (H) 15
- (I) 21

3. What is the measure, in degrees, of $\angle A$?

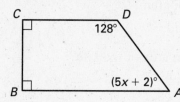

4. Which side is the longest?

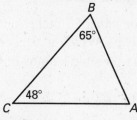

- (A) $\overline{AB}$
- (B) $\overline{AC}$
- (C) $\overline{BC}$
- (D) $\overline{CA}$

5. Which of the following statements describes the relationship between $\angle 1$ and $\angle 2$?

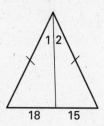

- (F) $m\angle 1 > m\angle 2$
- (G) $m\angle 1 < m\angle 2$
- (H) $m\angle 1 = m\angle 2$
- (I) $\angle 1 \cong \angle 2$

6. What value of x will make the polygon a parallelogram?

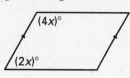

- (A) 30
- (B) 60
- (C) 120
- (D) 180

Name _____ Date _____

Module Test

For use after Module 5

MULTIPLE CHOICE   In Exercises 1–8, fill in the bubble for the correct answer.

1. A triangle has one side of 7 inches and another of 10 inches. Which is the correct description of the possible lengths of the third side?

    (A) greater than 17 inches

    (B) greater than 3 inches and less than 17 inches

    (C) less than 3 inches

    (D) greater than 6 inches and less than 9 inches

2. Which statement can you prove about the angle measures in the diagram below?

    (F) $m\angle CAD > m\angle DAB$

    (G) $m\angle C < m\angle A$

    (H) $m\angle DAC = m\angle DAB$

    (I) $m\angle ADC > m\angle ADB$

3. What is the value of x?

    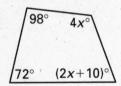

    (A) 28

    (B) 30

    (C) 120

    (D) 186

4. In parallelogram $PQRS$, $m\angle Q = 58°$. What is $m\angle R$?

    (F) 32°

    (G) 58°

    (H) 122°

    (I) 180°

5. For any rhombus $EFGH$, which statement is always true?

    (A) $EG = FH$

    (B) $m\angle G = m\angle H$

    (C) $EF = FG$

    (D) all of these

6. In rectangle $WXYZ$, if $XY = 6y - 4$ and $WZ = 4y$, then what is XY?

    (F) 0.4

    (G) 2

    (H) 6

    (I) 8

7. The vertices of quadrilateral $ABCD$ are $A(0, 0)$, $B(2, 4)$, $C(8, 4)$, and $D(6, 0)$. What type of quadrilateral is $ABCD$?

    (A) rhombus

    (B) kite

    (C) parallelogram

    (D) trapezoid

8. What is the area of the kite?

    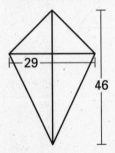

    (F) 334 square units

    (G) 444 square units

    (H) 667 square units

    (I) 1334 square units

Converse of the Pythagorean Theorem

Support for Benchmarks MA.C.2.4.1, MA.C.3.4.1

EXAMPLE **Tell whether the triangle is a right triangle.**

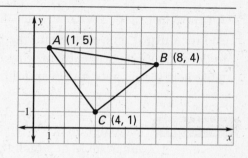

Use the Distance Formula to find AB, AC, and BC.

$AB = \sqrt{(1-8)^2 + (5-4)^2} = 5\sqrt{2}$

$AC = \sqrt{(1-4)^2 + (5-1)^2} = 5$

$BC = \sqrt{(4-8)^2 + (1-4)^2} = 5$

Now use the Converse of the Pythagorean Theorem to see whether the sides satisfy the equation $c^2 = a^2 + b^2$.

$(5\sqrt{2})^2 \stackrel{?}{=} 5^2 + 5^2$

$5^2 \cdot (\sqrt{2})^2 \stackrel{?}{=} 5^2 + 5^2$

$25 \cdot 2 \stackrel{?}{=} 25 + 25$

$50 = 50 \checkmark$

The triangle is a right triangle.

Exercises

1. Which set of numbers could represent the side lengths of a right triangle?

   (A) 2, 10, 12   (B) 4, $\sqrt{67}$, 81   (C) 10, 49, 50   (D) $\sqrt{13}$, 6, 7

2. Which set of numbers could NOT represent the side lengths of a right triangle?

   (F) $\sqrt{15}$, 7, 8   (G) 12, 18, 22   (H) 8, 15, 17   (I) 50, 120, 130

3. Points $R(8, -3)$ and $S(1, 4)$ are two of the three points of a right triangle. Which of the following points could NOT be the third point?

   (A) $W(1, -3)$ (B) $X(12, 1)$ (C) $Y(10, 3)$ (D) $Z(8, 4)$

In Exercises 4 and 5, use the following information.

If the square of the longest side of a triangle is less than the sum of the squares of the other two sides, then the triangle is acute. If the square of the longest side of a triangle is greater than the sum of the squares of the other two sides, then the triangle is obtuse.

4. Name a value of x that would make the triangle acute.

5. Name a value of x that would make the triangle obtuse.

Name _____ Date _____

Function Tables

Support for Benchmark MA.D.1.4.1

> A **function** is a relationship between two quantities, called the **input**
> and the **output**. For each input, there is exactly one output. One way
> to describe a function is by making an **input-output table**. Such a
> table lists the outputs for several different inputs.

EXAMPLE   The diagram below gives the first five square numbers. Make an input-
output table in which the input is the figure number n, and the output is
the square number S. Then find the output for an input of 6.

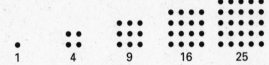

1   4   9   16   25

Figure 1   Figure 2   Figure 3   Figure 4   Figure 5

Input n	Output S
1	1
2	4
3	9
4	16
5	25
6	

Solution

First make an input-output table. You can see from the table
that the output is the square of the input. An input of 6
would give an output of 36.

Exercises

1. Michael stacks soup cans in the following manner, adding cans to the
   right of the stack and top of the stack each round. How many cans will
   be in the fifth round?

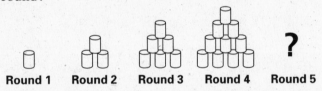

Round 1   Round 2   Round 3   Round 4   Round 5

   (A) 13   (B) 14   (C) 15   (D) 16

2. What is the next number in the sequence: 0.5, 3, 5.5, 8, 10.5, ___ ?

   (F) 12.5   (G) 13   (H) 13.5   (I) 14

Find the missing value(s) in the input-output table.

3.

Input x	1	2	3	4	5
Output y	$\frac{1}{4}$	$\frac{1}{12}$	$\frac{1}{36}$	$\frac{1}{108}$	

4. Rule: $5x^3 - y = 0$

Input x	-2	-1	0	1	2
Output y					

GRIDDED RESPONSE   In Exercises 9–15, grid the correct answer on the separate gridding sheet.

9. The measures of three angles of a quadrilateral are 50°, 122°, and 81°. How many degrees does the fourth angle measure?

10. What value of x will make the polygon a parallelogram?

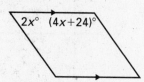

11. In rectangle $ABCD$, $m\angle A = (3x - 27)°$ and $AB = 2x - 42$. How many units long is AB?

12. $EFGH$ is a kite. How many degrees does $\angle G$ measure?

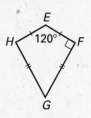

13. $JKLM$ is an isosceles trapezoid. By how many degrees is $\angle L$ greater than $\angle M$?

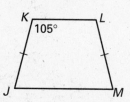

14. What is the area of the polygon in square inches?

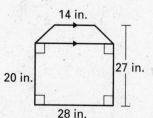

15. The area of a triangle is 42 square units. If the height is 21 units, how many units long is the base?

SHORT RESPONSE   In Exercise 16, write your answer on a separate piece of paper.

16. Of 4.1 meters and 19 centimeters, which measurement is more precise? Which measurement is more accurate? Explain your reasoning.

EXTENDED RESPONSE   In Exercise 17, write your answer to all parts on a separate piece of paper.

17. The diagram below shows quadrilateral $PQRS$ on a coordinate plane.

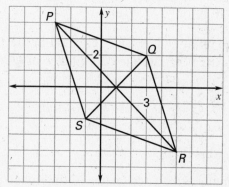

Part A Find the slopes of PQ, QR, RS, and SP. What do the slopes tell you?

Part B Find the slopes of PR and QS. What do the slopes tell you?

Part C What kind of special quadrilateral is $PQRS$? Use the most specific name. Explain your reasoning.

Mid-Module Quiz

For use after Lesson 7.4

1. What type of transformation is shown below?

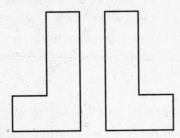

- Ⓐ slide
- Ⓑ reflection
- Ⓒ translation
- Ⓓ rotation

2. The point $Q(1, -2)$ is reflected in the x-axis. What are the coordinates of Q'?

- Ⓕ $(1, 2)$
- Ⓖ $(-1, 2)$
- Ⓗ $(-1, -2)$
- Ⓘ $(2, 1)$

3. What are the coordinates of the image of point C after a clockwise rotation of 90° about the origin?

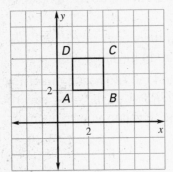

- Ⓐ $(-3, 4)$
- Ⓑ $(3, -4)$
- Ⓒ $(4, -3)$
- Ⓓ $(4, 3)$

4. What are the coordinates of the image of point A after a clockwise rotation of 270° about the origin?

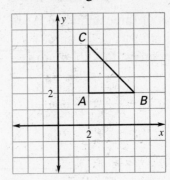

- Ⓕ $(-2, -2)$
- Ⓗ $(2, -2)$
- Ⓖ $(-2, 2)$
- Ⓘ $(2, 2)$

5. How many lines of symmetry does an equilateral triangle have?

6. What is the vector written in component form?

- Ⓐ $\langle -4, 3 \rangle$
- Ⓑ $\langle 3, 4 \rangle$
- Ⓒ $\langle 4, -3 \rangle$
- Ⓓ $\langle 4, 3 \rangle$

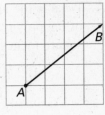

7. Consider the translation that is defined by the coordinate notation $(x, y) \rightarrow (x + 8, y - 4)$. What is the image of $(4, 7)$?

- Ⓕ $(-4, 11)$
- Ⓗ $(12, 3)$
- Ⓖ $(0, 15)$
- Ⓘ $(12, 7)$

Module Test

For use after Module 6

MULTIPLE CHOICE In Exercises 1–7, fill in the bubble for the correct answer.

1. What type of transformation is shown?

Ⓐ reflection

Ⓑ rotation

Ⓒ slide

Ⓓ translation

2. What are the coordinates of point *C* of the image after a clockwise rotation of 90° about the origin?

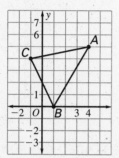

Ⓕ $(-4, -1)$

Ⓖ $(4, -1)$

Ⓗ $(-4, 1)$

Ⓘ $(4, 1)$

3. Consider the translation defined by $(x, y) \rightarrow (x + 5, y - 1)$. What is the image of $(2, 3)$?

Ⓐ $(-1, 4)$

Ⓑ $(7, 2)$

Ⓒ $(7, 8)$

Ⓓ $(8, 1)$

4. Which of the following is a reflection of the figure at the right?

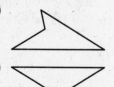

Ⓕ

Ⓖ

Ⓗ

Ⓘ

5. What are the coordinates of $A(4, 1)$ after a translation of $(x, y) \rightarrow (x, y + 3)$ and then a reflection in the *x*-axis?

Ⓐ $(-4, 4)$

Ⓑ $(4, -4)$

Ⓒ $(4, -1)$

Ⓓ $(4, 4)$

6. Which translation describes the translation shown below?

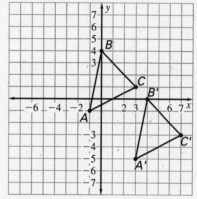

Ⓕ $(x, y) \rightarrow (x - 4, y - 4)$

Ⓖ $(x, y) \rightarrow (x - 4, y + 4)$

Ⓗ $(x, y) \rightarrow (x + 4, y - 4)$

Ⓘ $(x, y) \rightarrow (x + 4, y + 4)$

7. Find the coordinates of *B* after a translation of $(x, y) \rightarrow (x - 1, y + 2)$ and then a 90° clockwise rotation about the origin.

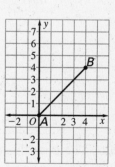

Ⓐ $(-6, 3)$

Ⓑ $(6, -3)$

Ⓒ $(6, 3)$

Ⓓ $(-6, 3)$

GRIDDED RESPONSE   In Exercises 8–13, grid the correct answer on the separate gridding sheet.

8. Find the measure of the angle of rotation, in degrees, that maps $\triangle XYZ$ onto $\triangle X''Y''Z''$.

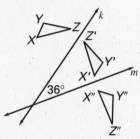

9. Hexagon $ABCDEF$ is regular. Suppose B is rotated clockwise about G. How many degrees is the rotation that maps B onto D?

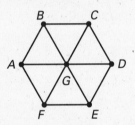

10. How many lines of symmetry does the figure have?

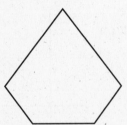

11. The coordinates of $X(3, 4z)$ after a translation of $(x, y) \rightarrow (x + 3, y - 4)$ are $(8 - z, 4)$. What is the value of z?

12. The coordinates of $A(2, 2c)$ after a reflection in the y-axis are $(1 - c, 6)$. What is the value of c?

13. The coordinates of $B(t - 3, -8)$ after a reflection in the y-axis are $(-2, -3 - t)$. What is the value of t?

SHORT RESPONSE   In Exercise 14, write your answer on a separate piece of paper.

14. Describe the composition of the transformations.

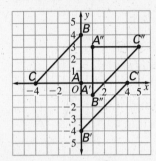

EXTENDED RESPONSE   In Exercise 15, answer all parts on a separate piece of paper.

15. Follow the steps below.

   Part A Draw $\triangle ABC$ by plotting and connecting the points $A(-1, 2)$, $B(3, 1)$, and $C(4, 4)$.

   Part B Reflect $\triangle ABC$ in the x-axis to obtain $\triangle A'B'C'$. Name the coordinates of the vertices of the reflection.

   Part C Rotate $\triangle A'B'C'$ 90° clockwise around the origin to obtain $\triangle A''B''C''$. Name the coordinates of the vertices of the rotation.

Cumulative Test

For use after Modules 1–6

MULTIPLE CHOICE   In Exercises 1–18, fill in the bubble for the correct answer.

1. The lengths of the two legs of an isosceles triangle are represented by the expressions $(9x - 40)$ and $(3x + 8)$. How long is each side?

   (A) 2 units   (C) 8 units
   (B) 4 units   (D) 32 units

2. Given $\angle A \cong \angle D$ and $\angle B \cong \angle E$, what is the value of x?

   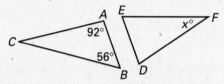

   (F) 32   (H) 124
   (G) 34   (I) 148

3. In triangle XYZ, the segments $\overline{XY}$ and $\overline{YZ}$ are congruent. A segment is drawn from point Y to point W, the midpoint of $\overline{XZ}$. Which of the following statements is NOT true?

   (A) $\overline{XW} \cong \overline{WZ}$

   (B) $\triangle XWY \cong \triangle ZWY$

   (C) $\overline{XW} \cong \overline{YZ}$

   (D) $\angle WXY \cong \angle WZY$

4. Which of the following properties makes the statement below **true**?

   If $m\angle ABC = m\angle DEF$ and $m\angle DEF = m\angle JKM$, then $m\angle ABC = m\angle JKM$.

   (F) Reflexive Property
   (G) Substitution Property
   (H) Symmetric Property
   (I) Transitive Property

5. What is the value of x?

   (A) 10
   (B) 15
   (C) 45
   (D) 60

   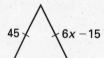

6. The midpoint of $\overline{CD}$ is $M(3, 1)$. One endpoint is $C(-2, -5)$. What are the coordinates of D?

   (F) $(6, 2)$
   (G) $(12, 10)$
   (H) $(2, 4)$
   (I) $(8, 7)$

7. In the diagram, $\overline{SV} \perp \overline{RT}$ and $\overline{VR} \cong \overline{VT}$. What is the length of SR?

   (A) 64
   (B) 84
   (C) 102
   (D) 148

   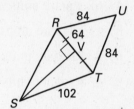

8. What is the average speed of a car that traveled 420 miles in 8 hours.

   (F) 105 mi/h
   (G) 105 h/mi
   (H) 52.5 mi/h
   (I) 52.5 h/mi

9. What is the value of x in the quadrilateral shown below?

   (A) 9
   (B) 23
   (C) 69
   (D) 207

   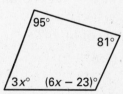

Name _____   Date _____

Cumulative Test

For use after Modules 1-6

10. What is the value of *m* in the parallelogram below?

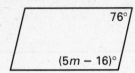

(F) 24   (H) 104

(G) 76   (I) 180

11. What is the area of the kite?

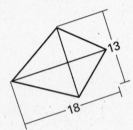

(A) 62 square units

(B) 117 square units

(C) 234 square units

(D) 468 square units

12. Suppose △*ABC* has vertices *A*(0, 0), *B*(4, 4), and *C*(4, 0). If △*ABC* is rotated 90° clockwise about the origin, what are the coordinates of *B'*?

(F) (−4, −4)

(G) (−4, 4)

(H) (4, −4)

(I) (4, 4)

13. Consider the translation that is defined by the coordinate notation $(x, y) \rightarrow (x + 2, y - 4)$. What is the image of (4, 6)?

(A) (−6, −2)

(B) (0, 8)

(C) (2, 6)

(D) (6, 2)

14. What are the coordinates of the image of *A*(−2, 3) after a translation of $(x, y) \rightarrow (x, y - 5)$ and a reflection in the *x*-axis?

(F) (−2, −2)   (H) (2, −2)

(G) (−2, 2)   (I) (2, 2)

15. What is the value of $(-3)^2 \div [8 + 1 - 2 \cdot 3]$?

(A) −9

(B) 3

(C) 27

(D) 135

16. The stem-and-leaf plot shows the ages of 20 people. How many people are over 20 years old?

```
0 | 6 8 9 5
1 | 2 2 5 8 9 6
2 | 1 4 4 5 8 2
3 | 3 2 0 1        Key: 3|3 = 33
```

(F) 4   (H) 10

(G) 9   (I) 16

17. Which list *is* in order from least to greatest?

(A) $-2, -\sqrt{2}, 0, \sqrt{8}, 2.3$

(B) $-2, -\sqrt{2}, 0, 2.3, \sqrt{8}$

(C) $-\sqrt{2}, -2, 0, 2.3, \sqrt{8}$

(D) $-\sqrt{2}, -2, 0, \sqrt{8}, 2.3$

18. If ∠2 and ∠3 are complementary and $m\angle 2 = 12°$, what is $m\angle 3$?

(F) 60°

(G) 78°

(H) 168°

(I) 348°

Name _____ Date _____

Cumulative Test

For use after Modules 1–6

GRIDDED RESPONSE In Exercises 19–32, grid the correct answer on a separate gridding sheet.

19. What is the measure of angle 3, in degrees?

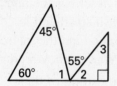

20. What is the measure of the exterior angle shown in degrees?

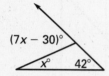

21. Given that $\angle K \cong \angle D$ and $\angle J \cong \angle C$, what is the value of s?

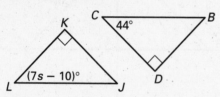

22. What is the value of y in the figure below?

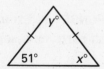

23. What is the value of y in the figure below?

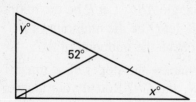

24. What is the area of the polygon in square inches?

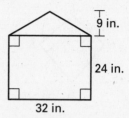

25. A bowling ball weighs about 256 **ounces**. How many **pounds** is this?

26. When Ben filled the gas tank of his car last week, the odometer showed 8901.6 miles. When Ben filled the gas tank this week, the odometer showed 9252.3 miles. His car used 14 gallons of gasoline during the week. Find the gasoline mileage to the nearest tenth of a mile per gallon.

27. What value of x will make the polygon a parallelogram?

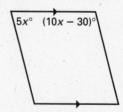

28. *EFGH* is a rhombus. What is the value of x?

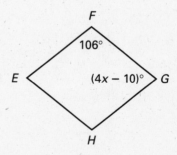

29. *EFGH* is a kite. What is $m\angle G$?

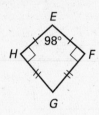

30. Determine the number that correctly completes the equation.

$6^4 \cdot 6^? = 6^{12}$

31. Consider the translation that is defined by the coordinate notation $(x, y) \rightarrow (x + 8, y - 6)$. What is the length of the vector in units?

32. Point *X* has a preimage of $(6, 2z - 8)$. After it is translated by $(x, y) \rightarrow (x + 5, y - 6)$, it has an image of $(2z - 3, 0)$. What is the value of *z*?

SHORT RESPONSE   In Exercises 33–34, write your answer on a separate piece of paper.

33. Your club holds a car wash for three hours to raise money for a charity. The equation $10x + 15y = 180$ describes the amount of time it takes to wash small and large vehicles respectively. Find the intercepts of the equation. What do they represent?

34. Describe the composition of the transformations.

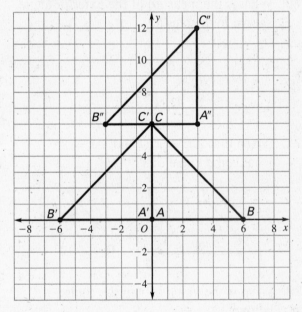

EXTENDED RESPONSE   In Exercise 35, write your answer to all parts on a separate piece of paper.

35. Triangle *ABC* has endpoints $A(0, 0)$, $B(0, 6)$, and $C(8, 0)$.

a. Find the midpoint of each side of triangle *ABC*. Let *P* be the midpoint of *AB*, let *Q* be the midpoint of *BC*, and let *R* be the midpoint of *AC*.

b. What are the slopes of segments *AQ*, *BR*, and *CP*? Round your answer to the nearest hundredth.

c. Is $\overline{AQ}$ perpendicular to $\overline{BC}$? Explain your answer.

MODULE 7 Mid-Module Quiz

For use after Lesson 8.5

1. The lengths of the sides of a triangle are in the extended ratio 5 : 7 : 9. The length of the longest side is 72 inches. What is the length of the shortest side?

(A) 5 in.

(B) 40 in.

(C) 56 in.

(D) 67 in.

2. The ratio of the width to the length of the rectangle, $AB:BC$, is 3:5. Solve for x in the figure below.

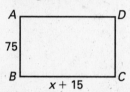

(F) 110

(G) 125

(H) 140

(I) 330

3. Given that $\dfrac{AB}{BD} = \dfrac{AC}{CE}$, what is BD?

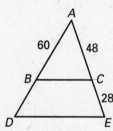

4. The two right triangles are similar. Find the value of x.

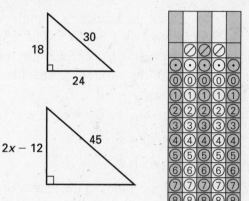

5. What is the value of x?

(A) 40

(B) 49

(C) 89

(D) 91

6. What is the the value of y?

(F) 80

(G) 60

(H) 26.5

(I) 0.75

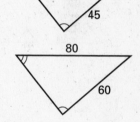

7. Find the distance labeled x.

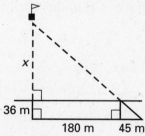

(A) 200 m

(B) 180 m

(C) 144 m

(D) 132 m

Module Test

For use after Module 7

MULTIPLE CHOICE In Exercises 1–8, fill in the bubble for the correct answer.

1. The lengths of the sides of a triangle are in the extended ratio $3 : 4 : 5$. The length of the shortest side is 39 feet. What are the lengths of the two remaining sides?
   (A) 4 ft and 5 ft
   (B) 12 ft and 15 ft
   (C) 40 ft and 50 ft
   (D) 52 ft and 65 ft

2. The ratio of the width to the length of the rectangle shown is $2 : 9$. What is the value of x?
   (F) 8
   (G) 20
   (H) 72
   (I) 144

3. The two triangles shown are similar. What is the value of y?

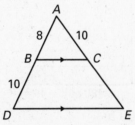

   (A) 2
   (B) 14
   (C) 32
   (D) 56

4. What is the length of $\overline{CE}$ in the triangle shown?
   (F) 8
   (G) 12
   (H) 12.5
   (I) 18.5

5. What is the distance labeled y in the diagram below?
   (A) 44 feet
   (B) 176 feet
   (C) 220 feet
   (D) 275 feet

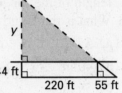

6. Find the distance across the pond shown if $CD = 60$ feet, $DX = 45$ feet, $AX = 90$ feet, and $\overline{AB} \| \overline{CD}$.
   (F) 65 feet
   (G) 105 feet
   (H) 120 feet
   (I) 150 feet

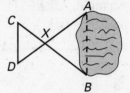

7. Does the diagram show an enlargement or a reduction? What is the scale factor shown?

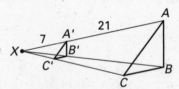

   (A) enlargement; $k = 4$
   (B) reduction; $k = 4$
   (C) reduction; $k = \dfrac{1}{3}$
   (D) reduction; $k = \dfrac{1}{4}$

8. Which postulate or theorem can be used to show that $\triangle ACE \sim \triangle BCD$?

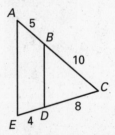

   (F) AA Similarity Postulate
   (G) SSS Similarity Theorem
   (H) SAS Similarity Theorem
   (I) Vertical Angles Theorem

GRIDDED RESPONSE   In Exercises 9–15, grid the correct answer on the separate gridding sheet.

9. In the triangle, the ratio $AC : AB$ is 4 : 7. What is the value of x?

10. Given that $\dfrac{SP}{SK} = \dfrac{SQ}{SJ}$, what is the length of $\overline{SQ}$?

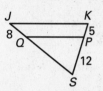

11. The two triangles shown are similar. What is the value of x?

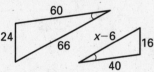

12. In the diagram below, what is HE?

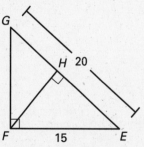

13. $\triangle P'Q'R'$ is the image of $\triangle PQR$ after a dilation. What is the value of x?

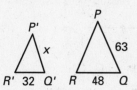

14. Use the origin as the center of dilation and a scale factor of $\dfrac{1}{2}$ to find the y-coordinate of K.

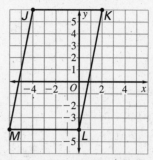

SHORT RESPONSE   In Exercise 15, write your answer on a separate piece of paper.

15. Determine whether the given information implies that $\overline{QS}\,\|\,\overline{PT}$. Explain your answer.

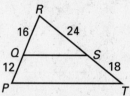

EXTENDED RESPONSE   In Exercise 16, answer all parts on a separate piece of paper.

16. Use the diagram below.

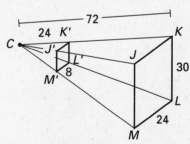

Part A Identify the dilation shown above.

Part B Find the scale factor of the dilation.

Part C What is the length of $\overline{K'L'}$? Explain how you found your answer.

Name _____ Date _____

Mid-Module Quiz

For use after Lesson 11.3

1. To the nearest tenth, what is the area of the triangle?

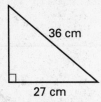

36 cm

27 cm

(A) 321.5 square centimeters

(B) 364.5 square centimeters

(C) 428.4 square centimeters

(D) 486 square centimeters

2. What is the value of x?

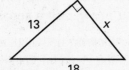

13   x

18

(F) $\sqrt{324}$

(G) 169

(H) 155

(I) $\sqrt{155}$

3. Which set of numbers represents the sides of a right triangle?

(A) 9, 15, $\sqrt{300}$

(B) 17, 12, $\sqrt{433}$

(C) 20, 20, $\sqrt{400}$

(D) 7, 11, $\sqrt{107}$

4. What is the value of x?

144° 110°

129°   110°

103° $x°$

5. The polygon shown is regular. What is the value of x?

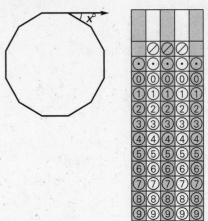

$x°$

6. The two hexagons are similar. What is the ratio of their areas?

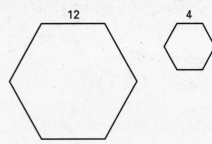

12   4

(F) 3 : 1

(G) 6 : 1

(H) 72 : 24

(I) 9 : 1

7. What is the value of y?

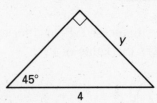

y

45°

4

(A) $2\sqrt{2}$

(B) $2\sqrt{3}$

(C) $4\sqrt{2}$

(D) $4\sqrt{3}$

Name _____   Date _____

Module Test

For use after Module 8

MULTIPLE CHOICE   In Exercises 1–8, fill in the bubble for the correct answer.

1. What is the area of the figure?

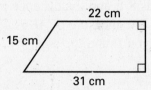

- Ⓐ 80 cm²
- Ⓑ 264 cm²
- Ⓒ 318 cm²
- Ⓓ 397.5 cm²

2. What is the length of side x?

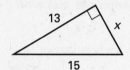

- Ⓕ 2
- Ⓖ $\sqrt{56}$
- Ⓗ 56
- Ⓘ 169

3. Which set of numbers represents the side lengths of a right triangle?

- Ⓐ 7, 16, $\sqrt{318}$
- Ⓑ 9, 14, $\sqrt{213}$
- Ⓒ 15, 11, $\sqrt{407}$
- Ⓓ 20, 20, $\sqrt{800}$

4. The two octagons are similar. What is the ratio of their areas?

- Ⓕ 9:2
- Ⓖ 9:4
- Ⓗ 81:2
- Ⓘ 81:4

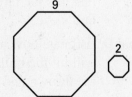

5. What is the length of $\overset{\frown}{AB}$?

- Ⓐ 7 ft
- Ⓑ 14 ft
- Ⓒ 14π ft
- Ⓓ 28π ft

6. In the diagram, the length of $\overset{\frown}{AB}$ is $(3y - 9)\pi$. What is the value of y?

- Ⓕ 0.6
- Ⓖ 6.2
- Ⓗ 9.6
- Ⓘ 75.36

7. What is the area of the shaded region?

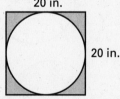

- Ⓐ $400 - 100\pi$ in.²
- Ⓑ 100π in.²
- Ⓒ 400 in.²
- Ⓓ $400 + 100\pi$ in.²

8. What is the probability that a randomly chosen point in the figure lies in the shaded region?

- Ⓕ 20%
- Ⓖ 30%
- Ⓗ 50%
- Ⓘ 72%

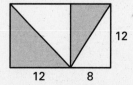

Name _____   Date _____

Module Test

For use after Module 8

GRIDDED RESPONSE In Exercises 9–14, grid the correct answer on the separate gridding sheet.

9. What is the value of x in degrees?

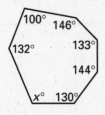

10. A regular polygon has 18 sides. What is the measure, in degrees, of each exterior angle?

11. What is the area of the triangle to the nearest square foot?

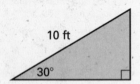

12. In $\triangle ABC$, $m\angle ABC = 90°$ and $\overline{AB} \cong \overline{CB}$. If $AC = 9\sqrt{2}$, then what is AB?

13. What is the length of $\overset{\frown}{XY}$? Round your answer to the nearest tenth.

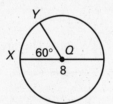

14. What is the area of the shaded region? Round your answer to the nearest whole number.

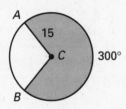

SHORT RESPONSE In Exercise 15, write your answer on a separate piece of paper.

15. Find the area of region $ABCD$. The length of radius RP is 8 ft and the distance from S to T is 4 ft. The measure of $\overset{\frown}{AB}$ is 45°. Explain how you found the area.

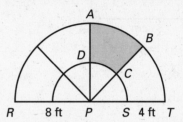

EXTENDED RESPONSE In Exercise 16, answer all parts on a separate piece of paper.

16. A circular target with a radius of 5 centimeters has a circular bull's eye with a diameter of 2 centimeters. Darts are thrown and hit the target at random.

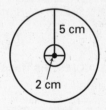

Part A What is the area of the entire target? Leave your answer in terms of π.

Part B What is the area of the bull's eye? Leave your answer in terms of π.

Part C What is the probability that a dart that hits the target will hit the bull's eye?

Part D Estimate how many times a dart will hit the bull's eye if 100 darts are thrown and hit the target at random.

Mid-Module Quiz

For use after Lesson 12.3

1. What type of regular polyhedron is shown at the right?

   (A) octahedron

   (B) cube

   (C) icosahedron

   (D) tetrahedron

2. How many edges does a rectangular prism have?

   (F) 4

   (G) 6

   (H) 8

   (I) 12

3. What is the surface area of the regular square pyramid?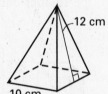

   (A) 240 square centimeters

   (B) 340 square centimeters

   (C) 344 square centimeters

   (D) 400 square centimeters

4. The surface area of the right cone below is 301.4 square inches. To the nearest inch, what is the height of the cone?

   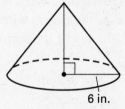

5. What is the surface area of a right rectangular prism with a height of 8 feet, length of 12 feet, and width of 2 feet?

   (F) 136 square feet

   (G) 192 square feet

   (H) 256 square feet

   (I) 272 square feet

6. What is the surface area, to the nearest square meter, of the right cylinder below?

   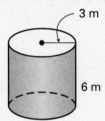

7. A cube has a surface area of 194.94 square inches. How many inches long is one of its edges?

Module Test

For use after Module 9

MULTIPLE CHOICE In Exercises 1–7, fill in the bubble for the correct answer.

1. What shape is the cross section of the cone as shown below?

   Ⓐ circle
   Ⓑ square
   Ⓒ triangle
   Ⓓ parallelogram

   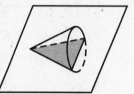

2. What is the sum of the number of vertices and the number of faces on the solid shown?

   Ⓕ 6
   Ⓖ 8
   Ⓗ 9
   Ⓘ 11

3. What is the surface area of the regular pyramid?

   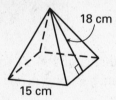

   18 cm

   15 cm

   Ⓐ 856 square centimeters
   Ⓑ 765 square centimeters
   Ⓒ 540 square centimeters
   Ⓓ 225 square centimeters

4. A regular pyramid has a triangular base with a base edge of 24 inches. Its height is 36 inches. What is the volume of the pyramid?

   Ⓕ 249.40 cubic inches
   Ⓖ 576.00 cubic inches
   Ⓗ 825.47 cubic inches
   Ⓘ 2,992.98 cubic inches

5. A bird feeder in the shape of a cone has a height of 15 centimeters and a diameter of 8 centimeters. ESTIMATE the number of cubic centimeters of bird seed it can hold.

   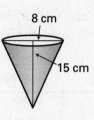

   8 cm

   15 cm

   Ⓐ 50 cubic centimeters
   Ⓑ 126 cubic centimeters
   Ⓒ 251 cubic centimeters
   Ⓓ 754 cubic centimeters

6. A smaller cube has a volume of 64 cubic feet and a larger cube has a volume of 343 cubic feet. What is the scale factor of the smaller cube to the larger cube?

   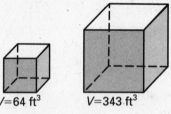

   $V=64$ ft^3 $V=343$ ft^3

   (not to scale)

   Ⓕ 16 : 49
   Ⓖ 4 : 7
   Ⓗ 64 : 343
   Ⓘ 2 : 7

7. A carton is being redesigned. What is the ratio of the volume of the carton with the new design to the volume of the carton with the old design?

   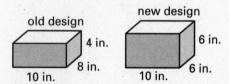

   old design   new design
   4 in.   6 in.
   8 in.
   10 in.   10 in.   6 in.

   Ⓐ 8 : 9
   Ⓑ 1 : 1
   Ⓒ 6 : 5
   Ⓓ 9 : 8

Module Test

For use after Module 9

GRIDDED RESPONSE In Exercises 8–12, grid the correct answer on the separate gridding sheet.

8. The surface area of the rectangular prism shown is 70 square inches. What is the height in inches of the prism?

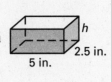

9. What is the surface area in square centimeters of a square pyramid whose base area is 25 square centimeters, and slant height is 7 centimeters?

10. What is the surface area in square inches of the right circular cone? Round to the nearest whole number.

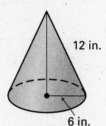

11. What is the volume of the regular pyramid in cubic centimeters?

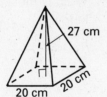

12. What is the surface area of the cylinder to the nearest square centimeter?

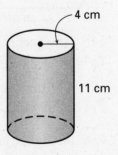

SHORT RESPONSE In Exercise 13, write your answer on a separate piece of paper.

13. Name the solid that could be made using the net below. Then find the surface area of the solid.

EXTENDED RESPONSE In Exercise 14, answer all parts on a separate piece of paper.

14. A concrete cylinder with a hollow center is used for the base of a street sign. The cylinders are right.

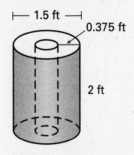

Part A Explain how to find the volume of concrete used in the base of the street sign.

Part B What is the volume of concrete in the base of the street sign? Round your answer to the nearest tenth of a cubic foot.

Part C Concrete weighs 145 pounds per cubic foot. How much does the concrete in the base of the street sign weigh?

Name _____ Date _____

Cumulative Test

For use after Modules 1–9

MULTIPLE CHOICE In Exercises 1–13, fill in the bubble for the correct answer.

1. The two triangles shown below are similar. What is the value of *p*?

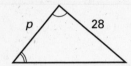

Ⓐ 12
Ⓑ 14
Ⓒ 24
Ⓓ 26

2. The width of the rectangle shown below is 15 inches. The ratio of the rectangle's width to its length is 3 : 7. What is the value of *x*?

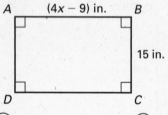

Ⓕ 11   Ⓗ 35
Ⓖ 12   Ⓘ 132

3. Which of the following correctly describes the dilation shown below and its scale factor, *k*?

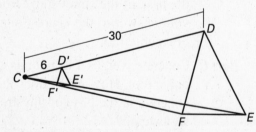

Ⓐ reduction; $k = \dfrac{1}{5}$
Ⓑ reduction; $k = 5$
Ⓒ enlargement; $k = \dfrac{1}{5}$
Ⓓ enlargement; $k = 5$

4. In the diagram below, what is the value of *x*?

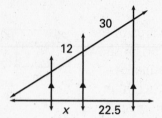

Ⓕ 9   Ⓗ 18
Ⓖ 10.5   Ⓘ 27

5. In triangle *QRS* shown below, what is the value of *x*?

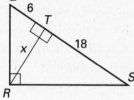

Ⓐ $6\sqrt{3}$
Ⓑ $6\sqrt{36}$
Ⓒ $36\sqrt{3}$
Ⓓ $3\sqrt{36}$

6. What is the area of the figure shown below?

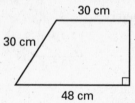

Ⓕ 216 square centimeters
Ⓖ 720 square centimeters
Ⓗ 936 square centimeters
Ⓘ 1,720 square centimeters

7. On the right triangle shown below, what is the length of side *x*?

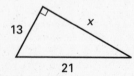

Ⓐ $4\sqrt{17}$ Ⓒ 68
Ⓑ $16\sqrt{17}$ Ⓓ $\sqrt{610}$

8. Which of the following equations *is* equivalent to the equation $hx + d = g$?

(F) $d = g + hx$

(G) $x = \dfrac{g - d}{h}$

(H) $x = g - d - h$

(I) $h = g - d - x$

9. Which of the following survey questions could produce a biased response?

(A) "How often do you buy lunch in the school cafeteria?"

(B) "Do you ride a bus to get to school?"

(C) "Do you prefer a talent show or a softball game as a fundraiser?"

(D) "Wouldn't building a new library be a good idea?"

10. What is the surface area of the regular pyramid shown below?

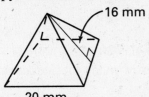

16 mm

20 mm

(F) 400 square millimeters

(G) 640 square millimeters

(H) 1,040 square millimeters

(I) 1,680 square millimeters

11. In the diagram below, what is the value of y? (Use $\pi \approx 3.14$.)

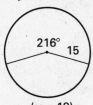

216° 15

$(y - 18)\pi$

(A) 12   (C) 37.68

(B) 30   (D) 94.2

12. If you randomly choose a point on the figure shown below, what is the probability that the point will lie in the shaded region?

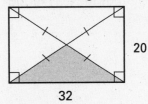

20

32

(F) 12%

(G) 25%

(H) 50%

(I) 96%

13. The dimensions of the right rectangular prism shown below are doubled. How many times larger is the volume of the new prism?

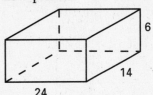

6

14

24

(A) $\dfrac{1}{2}$ (C) 4

(B) 2   (D) 8

Cumulative Test

1-9 Continued

For use after Modules 1-9

Name _____ Date _____

GRIDDED RESPONSE In Exercises 14–25, grid the correct answer on the separate gridding sheet.

14. What is the length of the legs of the right triangle below?

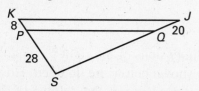

15. On the figure below, $\frac{SP}{SK} = \frac{SQ}{SJ}$. What is the length, in units, of $\overline{SQ}$?

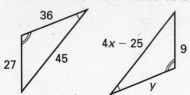

16. The two triangles shown below are similar. What is the value of x?

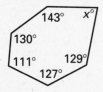

17. A car dealership has 387 cars that are last year's models. This represents 45% of its cars. How many cars does the car dealership have?

18. In the polygon shown below, what is the value of x, in degrees?

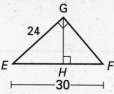

19. In the figure shown below, what is the length, in units, of EH?

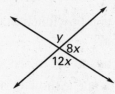

20. What is the value of x in the diagram below?

21. What is the length of $\overparen{XY}$ on the circle shown below? (Use $\pi \approx 3.14$.)

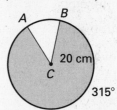

22. A polyhedron has 30 edges and 16 vertices. How many faces does it have?

23. What is the area, in square units, of the shaded region of the circle shown below? (Use $\pi \approx 3.14$.)

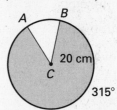

24. What is the length in inches, of the hypotenuse of a right triangle with leg lengths of 28 inches and 45 inches?

138 **Geometry**
Sunshine State Standards Support Book

Copyright © McDougal Littell,
a division of Houghton Mifflin Company

MODULES 1-9 Continued
Cumulative Test
For use after Modules 1–9

25. What is the volume, in cubic inches, of the cone shown below? (Use $\pi \approx 3.14$.)

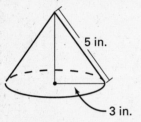

5 in.

3 in.

SHORT RESPONSE In Exercises 26 and 27, write your answer on a separate piece of paper.

26. Write a function rule that relates x and y. Explain how you found your answer.

Input x	−2	−1	0	1	2
Output y	−7	−5	−3	−1	1

27. Solve the linear system below. Explain how you can check your answer using a coordinate grid.

$$2x - y = -2$$
$$4x + y = 20$$

EXTENDED RESPONSE In Exercise 28, write your answer to all parts on a separate piece of paper.

28. You have $200 to spend on a health club membership. The initial fee to join is $50. There is a monthly fee of $32. For how many months can you be a member without spending more than $200?

Part A Write a variable expression for the total cost of a health club membership.

Part B Use the expression from Part A to write an inequality.

Part C Solve the inequality and check that the answer makes sense. Explain what the solution means in the situation.

Name _____ Date _____

Mid-Module Quiz

For use after Lesson 10.4

1. $\overleftrightarrow{AB}$ is tangent to $\odot C$ at B, and $\overleftrightarrow{AD}$ is tangent to $\odot C$ at D. What is the value of x?

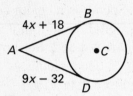

4x + 18

9x − 32

(A) 50
(B) 10
(C) 5
(D) 1

2. What value of x would make $\overleftrightarrow{AB}$ tangent to $\odot C$?

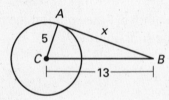

(F) 169
(G) 25
(H) 13
(I) 12

3. What is the measure of $\overset{\frown}{ABC}$?

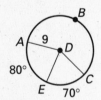

(A) 75°
(B) 150°
(C) 210°
(D) 280°

4. What is ED?

5. What is the value of y?

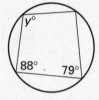

6. What is the measure of $\overset{\frown}{ABC}$?

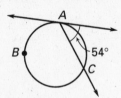

(F) 108°
(G) 180°
(H) 252°
(I) 306°

MULTIPLE CHOICE   In Exercises 1–8, fill in the bubble for the correct answer.

1. $\overleftrightarrow{AB}$ is tangent to $\odot C$ at B, and $\overleftrightarrow{AD}$ is tangent to $\odot C$ at D. What is the value of x?

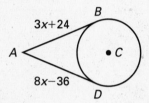

(A) 60   (C) 12

(B) 6   (D) 1

2. What value of x would make $\overleftrightarrow{AB}$ tangent to $\odot C$?

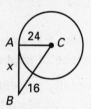

(F) 16   (H) 32

(G) 24   (I) 40

3. What is the measure of $\overset{\frown}{FHG}$?

(A) 120°

(B) 180°

(C) 240°

(D) 360°

4. What is the measure of $\overset{\frown}{DE}$?

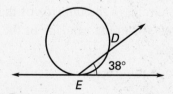

(F) 19°   (H) 57°

(G) 38°   (I) 76°

5. What is the value of x?

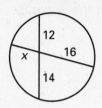

(A) 9   (C) 12

(B) 10.5   (D) 14

6. To the nearest tenth what is the value of x?

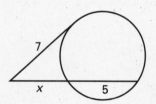

(F) 4.9   (H) 3.8

(G) 4.7   (I) 3.5

7. What is the radius of the circle with the equation $(x + 7)^2 + (y - 6)^2 = 49$?

(A) −1   (C) 7

(B) 6   (D) 49

8. What is the locus of points in the coordinate plane that are 6 units from the origin?

(F) the line $x = 6$

(G) the circle $x^2 + y^2 = 6$

(H) the circle $x^2 + y^2 = 36$

(I) the line $y = 6$

Name _____ Date _____

Module Test

For use after Module 10

GRIDDED RESPONSE In Exercises 9–16, grid the correct answer on the separate gridding sheet.

9. What is the value of *x*?

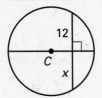

10. What is the measure of $\overarc{CE}$ in degrees?

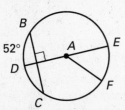

11. What is the value of *y*?

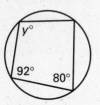

12. What is the value of *z*?

13. What is the measure of ∠1 in degrees?

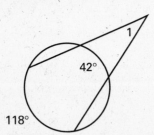

14. What is the value of *x* to the nearest tenth?

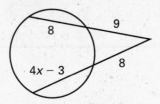

15. What is the value of *x*?

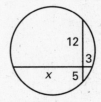

16. The equation of a circle is $(x + 1)^2 + (y - 2)^2 = 9$. What is the radius of the circle?

SHORT RESPONSE In Exercise 17, write your answer on a separate piece of paper.

17. Circles *X* and *Y* are externally tangent. The radius of circle *X* is 12 inches and the radius of circle *Y* is 8 inches. What is the locus of all points that are a distance of *XY* from point *X*?

EXTENDED RESPONSE In Exercise 18, answer all parts on a separate piece of paper.

18. The equation of a circle is $(x + 3)^2 + (y - 6)^2 = 16$.

Part A Give the coordinates of the center and the length of the radius.

Part B Tell whether the point (0, 0) is on the circle, in the *interior* of the circle, or in the *exterior* of the circle.

Part C Graph the circle.

Name _____ Date _____

Mid-Module Quiz

For use after Lesson 9.6

1. What is *CD*?

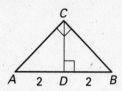

(A) 2

(B) $2\sqrt{2}$

(C) 4

(D) 8

2. Find *x*, the length of $\overline{BD}$.

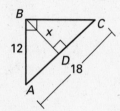

(F) $4\sqrt{3}$

(G) 8

(H) $4\sqrt{5}$

(I) $6\sqrt{5}$

3. Which expression represents the value of *x*?

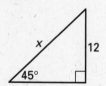

(A) $\dfrac{\sin 45°}{12}$

(B) $12 \sin 45°$

(C) $12 \cos 45°$

(D) $\dfrac{12}{\sin 45°}$

4. What is the value of *y* rounded to the nearest tenth?

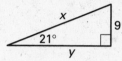

5. What is the measure of ∠*ABC* rounded to the nearest tenth of a degree?

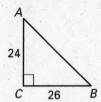

6. What is the value of *q* rounded to the nearest tenth?

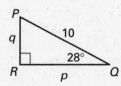

(F) 4.7

(G) 5.3

(H) 8.8

(I) 21.3

Module Test

For use after Module 11

MULTIPLE CHOICE In Exercises 1–8, fill in the bubble for the correct answer.

1. What is *DB*?

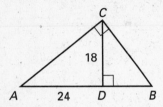

Ⓐ 11.8   Ⓒ 20

Ⓑ 13.5   Ⓓ 24

2. What is the value of *d* rounded to the nearest tenth?

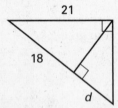

Ⓕ 3.6   Ⓗ 7.2

Ⓖ 6.5   Ⓘ 10.8

3. What is the value of *s* rounded to the nearest tenth?

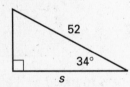

Ⓐ 29.1   Ⓒ 43.1

Ⓑ 35.1   Ⓓ 62.7

4. What is the value of *a*?

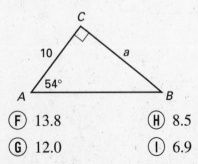

Ⓕ 13.8   Ⓗ 8.5

Ⓖ 12.0   Ⓘ 6.9

5. What is the sum of the vectors $\langle 2, 8 \rangle$ and $\langle 4, -3 \rangle$?

Ⓐ $\langle 6, 11 \rangle$

Ⓑ $\langle -6, 5 \rangle$

Ⓒ $\langle -2, 5 \rangle$

Ⓓ $\langle 6, 5 \rangle$

6. What is the area of the polygon rounded to the nearest tenth?

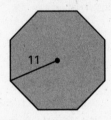

Ⓕ 342.2 square units

Ⓖ 171.1 square units

Ⓗ 85.6 square units

Ⓘ 42.8 square units

7. What is the area of the triangle?

Ⓐ $16\sqrt{3}$ Ⓒ $4\sqrt{3}$

Ⓑ $16\sqrt{2}$ Ⓓ $4\sqrt{2}$

8. The perimeter of a square is 32 inches. What is the length of a diagonal of the square to the nearest tenth of an inch?

Ⓕ 9.4 inches

Ⓖ 11.3 inches

Ⓗ 13.6 inches

Ⓘ 22.6 inches

Name _____   Date _____

Module Test

For use after Module 11

GRIDDED RESPONSE   In Exercises 9–15,
grid the correct answer on the separate
gridding sheet.

9. Find the value of z. Round your answer to
    the nearest tenth.

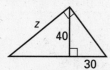

z 40 30

10. Find the value of f. Round your answer to
    the nearest tenth.

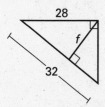

28 f 32

11. Find the value of v. Round your answer to
    the nearest tenth.

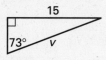

15 73° v

12. Find the measure of $\angle ABC$, in degrees.
    Round to the nearest tenth.

A 30 C 33 B

13. Find the area of the triangle. Round to the
    nearest tenth.

12 12 12

14. Find the perimeter of the regular polygon.
    Round to the nearest whole number.

12

15. Find the area of the regular polygon.
    Round to the nearest whole number.

14

SHORT RESPONSE   In Exercise 16, write
your answer on a separate piece of paper.

16. Copy the vectors $\vec{u}$ and $\vec{v}$. Write the
    component form of each vector. Then
    find the sum $\vec{u} + \vec{v}$ and draw the
    vector $\vec{u} + \vec{v}$.

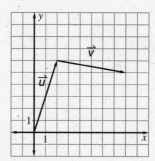

EXTENDED RESPONSE   In Exercise 17,
answer all parts on a separate piece of
paper.

17. A swimmer heads due east across a river
    at a speed of 4 miles per hour. The
    current of the river is flowing due north at
    a speed of 6 miles per hour.

    Part A Use vectors $\vec{u}$ and $\vec{v}$ to represent
             the velocities of the swimmer and
             the river. Write the vectors in
             component form.

    Part B Let $\vec{s} = \vec{u} + \vec{v}$. Write $\vec{s}$ in
             component form. What does $\vec{s}$
             represent?

    Part C Draw vectors $\vec{u}, \vec{v}$, and $\vec{s}$ in a
             coordinate plane.

1. The perpendicular bisectors of $\triangle RST$ meet at point D. What is DR?

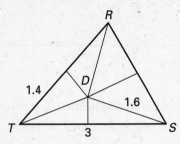

   A) 1.4
   B) 1.5
   C) 1.6
   D) 3

2. P is the centroid of $\triangle DEF$. What is the length of $\overline{PH}$?

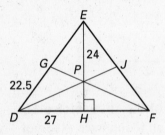

   F) 12
   G) 13.5
   H) 16
   I) 24

Use the diagram below for Exercises 3 and 4.

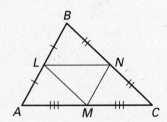

3. If $LM = 6x + 2$ and $BC = 9x + 10$, what is the value of x?

   A) 2
   B) 2.67
   C) 14
   D) 28

4. If $MN = 10x + 5$ and $AB = 15x + 37$, what is AB?

5. What is the length of $\overline{MN}$?

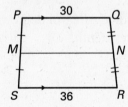

6. When you join the midpoints of the sides of any quadrilateral, what special quadrilateral is formed?

   F) trapezoid
   G) square
   H) kite
   I) parallelogram

MULTIPLE CHOICE   In Exercises 1–6, fill in the bubble for the correct answer.

1. The angle bisectors of $\triangle XYZ$ meet at point W. What is the length of $\overline{WB}$?

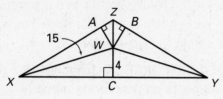

(A) 15   (C) 4

(B) 8   (D) 2

2. In the triangle below, F is the centroid, $\overline{EH}$ and $\overline{DF}$ are perpendicular, and $DE = FE$. What is the length of $\overline{EH}$?

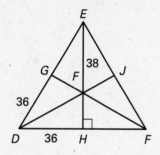

(F) 19   (H) 57

(G) 38   (I) 72

3. In triangle ABC, the points L, M, and N are the midpoints of the sides. If $LM = 8x + 4$ and $BC = 12x + 24$, then what is numerical value of LM?

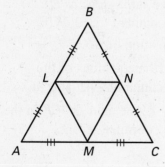

(A) 4   (C) 32

(B) 16   (D) 36

4. What is the angle of rotation that maps $\triangle PQR$ onto $\triangle P''Q''R''$?

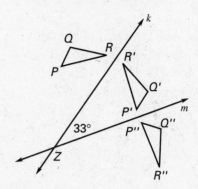

(F) 11°

(G) 33°

(H) 66°

(I) 99°

5. What is the component form of the vector shown below?

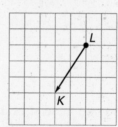

(A) $\langle -2, -3 \rangle$

(B) $\langle -2, 3 \rangle$

(C) $\langle 2, -3 \rangle$

(D) $\langle 2, 3 \rangle$

6. A polyhedron has 20 faces and 30 edges. How many vertices does it have?

(F) 12   (H) 32

(G) 22   (I) 48

GRIDDED RESPONSE   In Exercises 7–10, grid the correct answer on the separate gridding sheet.

7. In triangle *ABC*, the points *M* and *N* are the midpoints of the sides. If *MN* = $8x + 17$ and *AB* = $18x + 20$, then what is numerical value of *AB*?

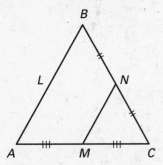

8. What is the value of *x*?

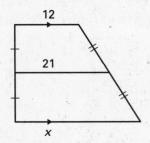

9. What is the area, in square meters, of the trapezoid?

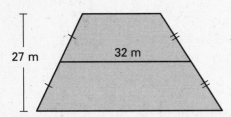

10. A solid has 8 faces: 2 hexagons and 6 rectangles. How many vertices does the solid have?

SHORT RESPONSE   In Exercise 11, write your answer on a separate piece of paper.

11. Using a straightedge, draw a line and label it *l*. Draw a point not on the line and label it *P*. Use a compass to construct a line perpendicular to *l* that passes through *P*. Explain the steps you took.

EXTENDED RESPONSE   In Exercise 12, answer all parts on a separate piece of paper.

12. The diagram below shows the points *D*(3, 5), *E*(4, 3), and *F*(5, 6), which are midpoints of the sides of △*ABC*. Use the directions to reconstruct △*ABC*.

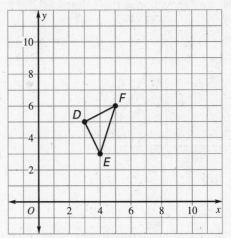

Part A Find the slope of each midsegment.

Part B The line containing $\overline{CB}$ has the same slope as $\overline{DE}$. $\overline{CB}$ contains *F*(5, 6). Write an equation of $\overleftrightarrow{CB}$.

Part C Write the equations of the lines containing $\overline{AB}$ and $\overline{AC}$.

Part D Draw △*ABC* and △*DEF* in the same coordinate plane.

GRADE **10**

FCAT Diagnostic Test 1

Use Exs. 1–44 to assess Grade 10 FCAT benchmarks only.
Use Exs. 1–52 to assess the content of the complete Geometry course.

Record your answers on the separate answer sheets.

1. Mike drew the figures below. If he continues the pattern, which figure will he draw next?

A.

  C.

B. **D.**

2. A billiards ball bounces off the side rail so that ∠1 and ∠2 are congruent, and the sum of their measures is 136°. Find the measure of ∠4.

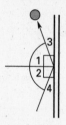

F. 19°   **H.** 34°
G. 22°   **I.** 68°

3. Which of the following is NOT a true statement about the expression $-|-38| + (-6)^2$?

A. It is equivalent to $6^2 - 38$.
B. Its value is less than $(-6)^2$.
C. It is equivalent to $-38 + (-36)$.
D. Its value is less than zero.

4. Evaluate the expression $(7 + 3)^2 - 4 \cdot 2$.

F. 8
G. 28
H. 92
I. 192

5. If Joseph located his school at (1, 6) on a coordinate plane, his house would be located at (13, 1). If each unit is equal to $\frac{1}{4}$ of a mile, what is the distance in miles between his house and the school?

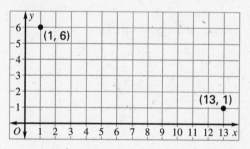

6. If $\overline{AB} \cong \overline{BC}$ and $\overline{CD} \cong \overline{BC}$, then what is the value of x?

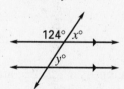

7. In the diagram, what is the value of y?

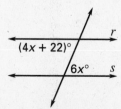

8. Find the value of x that makes $r \parallel s$.

9. | THINK | SOLVE | EXPLAIN | What is the measure in degrees of ∠AXF? Explain your reasoning.

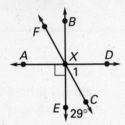

10. Lines *a* and *b* are parallel in the diagram. Line *c* is a transversal. What is the value of *x*?

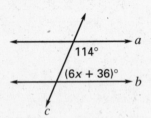

A. 3

B. 5

C. 8

D. 25

11. Which of the following is an equation of a line perpendicular to $y + 8 = -5x$?

F. $y - 8 = -\frac{1}{5}x$

G. $y + 8 = -5x$

H. $y + 8 = 5x$

I. $y + 8 = \frac{1}{5}x$

12. Which of the following lists 2.7, $2\frac{2}{3}$, and $\sqrt{8}$ in order from **least** to **greatest**?

A. $\sqrt{8}$, $2\frac{2}{3}$, 2.7

B. $2\frac{2}{3}$, $\sqrt{8}$, 2.7

C. $2\frac{2}{3}$, 2.7, $\sqrt{8}$

D. 2.7, $2\frac{2}{3}$, $\sqrt{8}$

13. Given $\angle A \cong \angle D$ and $\angle B \cong \angle E$, find the value of *x*.

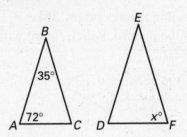

F. 35

H. 73

G. 37

I. 107

14. | THINK | SOLVE | EXPLAIN | Find the slope of $\overleftrightarrow{AC}$ and the slope of $\overleftrightarrow{BD}$. Decide whether $\overleftrightarrow{AC}$ is perpendicular to $\overleftrightarrow{BD}$. Explain your reasoning.

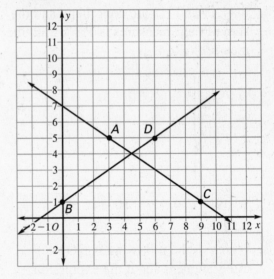

15. The numbers of tickets sold to see a movie for 8 weekend showings at a theater were 47, 55, 68, 64, 68, 50, 58, and 70. Which of the following correctly lists the mean, median, and mode of this data?

A. mean: 60; median: 58; mode: 68

B. mean: 60; median: 68; mode: 61

C. mean: 60; median: 61; mode: 68

D. mean: 61; median: 60; mode: 61

16. Compared to the graph of $y = 3x$, the graph of $y = 3x - 4$

  F. has a greater slope.

  G. has a lesser slope.

  H. has a greater y-intercept.

  I. has a greater x-intercept.

17. Use the bar graph of polling results for 3 weeks prior to an election. Which of the following statements is verified by the graph?

Which Candidate Do You Prefer?

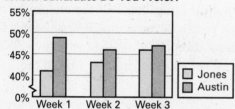

  A. About twice as many people preferred Austin as Jones in Week 1.

  B. Jones was preferred by 45% in Week 2.

  C. The percent of people who preferred Austin has decreased each week.

  D. Jones is getting closer to Austin in the polls.

18. A mouse can run at a speed of 8 miles per hour. Choose the best estimate of the number of **feet** a mouse can run in one **minute** at that speed.

  F. about 500 feet

  G. about 600 feet

  H. about 700 feet

  I. about 800 feet

19. THINK SOLVE EXPLAIN Place a 5-unit by 7-unit rectangle in a coordinate plane and find the length of a diagonal drawn from opposite corners. Explain how you found the length.

20. Rectangle $WXYZ$ has diagonal $\overline{WY}$. Which statement correctly describes the congruence of the triangles formed?

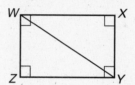

  A. $\triangle WXY \cong \triangle YZW$

  B. $\triangle WXY \cong \triangle YWZ$

  C. $\triangle WXY \cong \triangle WYZ$

  D. $\triangle WXY \cong \triangle WZY$

21. A school club is organizing a talent show to raise money. To spark interest, the students will sell the first 50 tickets at a $4 discount. The remaining 700 tickets will be sold at full price. The students expect to collect at least $5800 from ticket sales for this event. If x represents the full ticket price, which inequality does NOT represent this situation?

  F. $700x + 200 \geq 5800$

  G. $750x - 200 \geq 5800$

  H. $700x + 50(x - 4) \geq 5800$

  I. $700x + 50x - 200 \geq 5800$

22. Solve for x.

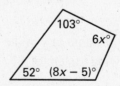

  A. 15

  B. 21

  C. 63

  D. 118

FCAT Diagnostic Test 1

23. Find the area of the kite.

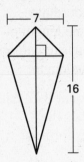

- **F.** 28 square units
- **G.** 56 square units
- **H.** 112 square units
- **I.** 224 square units

24. Solve for y.

25. 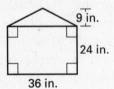 Find the area of the polygon in square inches.

26. 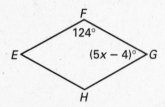 The figure *EFGH* is a rhombus. Solve for x.

27. What is the value of y in the solution of the following system of equations?

$$x - y = 8$$
$$3x - y = 30$$

28. Consider the translation that is defined by the coordinate notation $(x, y) \rightarrow (x - 5, y + 2)$. What is the image of $(6, -4)$?

- **A.** $(-1, -6)$
- **C.** $(1, -2)$
- **B.** $(-1, 6)$
- **D.** $(1, 2)$

29. How many lines of symmetry does a rectangle have if the rectangle is not a square?

- **F.** none
- **H.** two
- **G.** one
- **I.** four

30. Find the coordinates of the endpoints of the image of the segment below after a translation of $(x, y) \rightarrow (x + 2, y - 5)$ and a 90° clockwise rotation around the origin.

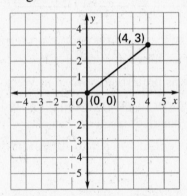

- **A.** $(-6, -2)$ and $(-2, -5)$
- **B.** $(-5, -2)$ and $(-2, -6)$
- **C.** $(2, -5)$ and $(5, -9)$
- **D.** $(5, 2)$ and $(2, 6)$

31. A survey reports that when people were asked to choose a number from 1 to 10, 4.2% chose the number 1. If 4000 people were asked, which of the following is a reasonable estimate of the number of people that chose the number 1?

- **F.** about 40
- **H.** about 400
- **G.** about 160
- **I.** about 1600

32. Which conditions are NOT sufficient to prove that $\triangle ABC$ is similar to $\triangle PQR$?

A. $m\angle A = m\angle P$ and $m\angle B = m\angle Q$

B. $m\angle B = m\angle Q$, and $\dfrac{AB}{PQ} = \dfrac{BC}{QR}$

C. $\dfrac{AB}{PQ} = \dfrac{BC}{QR}$

D. $\dfrac{AB}{PQ} = \dfrac{BC}{QR} = \dfrac{AC}{PR}$

33. A street lamp casts a shadow that is 21 feet long. At the same time, a person who is 6 feet tall casts a shadow that is 9 feet long. The triangles below represent this situation.

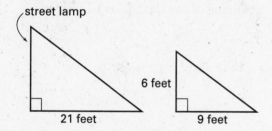

How tall is the street lamp?

F. 6 feet

G. 14 feet

H. 18 feet

I. 31.5 feet

34. A company gave all of its employees a 2.5% pay increase one year. One employee earned an annual salary of $50,000 before the pay increase. What was the employee's annual salary after the pay increase?

A. $50,002.50

B. $51,250

C. $62,500

D. $125,000

35. You choose a marble at random from a jar holding 4 red, 2 green, and 2 yellow marbles. You also choose a coin at random from a bag holding 1 quarter and 2 dimes. What is the probability that you choose a red marble and a dime?

F. $\dfrac{1}{3}$

G. $\dfrac{1}{2}$

H. $\dfrac{6}{11}$

I. $\dfrac{2}{3}$

36. Find the area of the figure to the nearest tenth of a square centimeter.

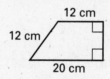

A. 288.4 square centimeters

B. 230.8 square centimeters

C. 178.9 square centimeters

D. 143.1 square centimeters

37.

THINK	The table shows the total
SOLVE	number of movie screens, in
EXPLAIN	millions, in the United States from 1980 to 2000.

year	1980	1985	1990	1995	2000
screens (millions)	18	21	24	28	37

Part A Make a scatter plot of the data in the table.

Part B On the scatter plot, as time passes, what happens to the number of movie screens?

Part C Predict the number of movie screens in 2005. Explain how you made your prediction.

38. Find the length of $\overset{\frown}{AB}$ in feet. Round to the nearest tenth of a foot. Use 3.14 for π.

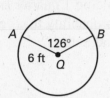

39. Find the area of the shaded region in square inches. Use 3.14 for π. Round your answer to the nearest tenth.

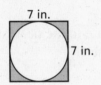

40. In the diagram, $\overleftrightarrow{CP} \perp \overline{AB}$ and $\overline{AC} \cong \overline{BC}$. Find the perimeter of $\triangle ABC$.

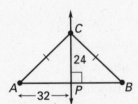

41. Carolyn is painting all the surfaces on the inside and the outside of a shoe box except for the lid. The box is in the shape of a rectangular prism that is 12 inches long, 6 inches wide, and 4 inches high. How many square inches will she be covering with paint?

42. A sphere has a radius of 11 feet. What is the area of a planar cross section that passes through the center of the sphere?

   F. 11π square feet

   G. $11\pi^2$ square feet

   H. 22π square feet

   I. 121π square feet

43. The table shows some values of a function.

Input x	−2	−1	0	1	2
Output y	4	2	0	−2	?

What is the value of y when $x = 2$?

   A. -4

   B. -1

   C. 2

   D. 4

44. THINK SOLVE EXPLAIN Name the solid that could be made using the net below. Then find the surface area and the volume of the solid. Use 3.14 for π.

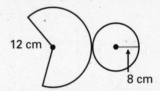

45. In the circle shown, what is the value of x?

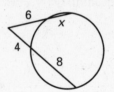

   F. 1

   G. $\dfrac{3}{2}$

   H. 2

   I. 3

46. Which of the following is an equation of a circle with center $(3, -5)$ and a radius of 8?

   A. $(x - 3)^2 + (y - 5)^2 = 64$

   B. $(x + 3)^2 + (y - 5)^2 = 64$

   C. $(x - 3)^2 + (y + 5)^2 = 64$

   D. $(x - 3)^2 - (y - 5)^2 = 64$

FCAT Diagnostic Test 1

47. Let $\vec{w} = \langle 2, -5 \rangle$ and $\vec{z} = \langle -4, 2 \rangle$. Find $\vec{w} + \vec{z}$.

   F. $\langle 2, -3 \rangle$

   G. $\langle -2, -3 \rangle$

   H. $\langle -2, 3 \rangle$

   I. $\langle -3, 2 \rangle$

48. In the triangle below, tan X is equal to which of the following?

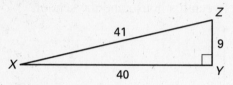

   A. $\dfrac{9}{40}$

   B. $\dfrac{9}{41}$

   C. $\dfrac{40}{41}$

   D. $\dfrac{41}{40}$

49. The points E, F, and G lie on a circle. Segment EG is a diameter of the circle. What is the measure of $\angle EFG$ in degrees?

50. Find the area of the triangle to the nearest square unit.

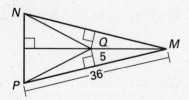

51. The perpendicular bisectors of the sides of $\triangle MNP$ meet at point Q. Find QN. Round your answer to the nearest tenth.

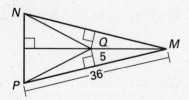

52. Use the diagram below.

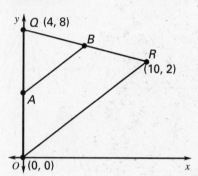

Part A Find the midpoint A of $\overline{OQ}$ and the midpoint B of $\overline{QR}$. Show your work.

Part B Using the Midpoint Theorem, what can you conclude about the relationship between $\overline{AB}$ and $\overline{OR}$?

Part C Use your results from Part A to verify your conclusions in Part B.

GRADE 10 FCAT Diagnostic Test 2

Use Exs. 1–44 to assess Grade 10 FCAT benchmarks only.
Use Exs. 1–52 to assess the content of the complete Geometry course.

Record your answers on the separate answer sheets.

1. Jake drew the figures below. If he continues the pattern, which figure will he draw next?

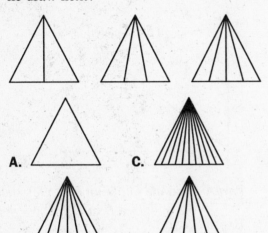

2. A billiards ball bounces off the side rail, so that $\angle 1$ and $\angle 2$ are congruent, and the sum of their measures is 118°. Find the measure of $\angle 4$.

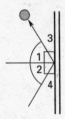

F. 29°   H. 58°
G. 31°   I. 61°

3. Which of the following is NOT a true statement about the expression $-|-44| + (-2)^2$?

A. It is equivalent to $2^2 - 44$.
B. Its value is less than $(-2)^2$.
C. It is equivalent to $-44 + (-4)$.
D. Its value is less than zero.

4. Evaluate the expression $(10 - 3)^2 + 3 \cdot 6$.

F. 19   H. 67
G. 24   I. 312

5. If Alex located school at (2, 3) on a coordinate plane, his house would be located at (10, 9). If each unit is equal to $\frac{1}{10}$ of a mile, what is the distance in miles between his house and the school?

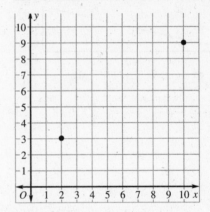

6. If $\overline{AB} \cong \overline{BC}$ and $\overline{BC} \cong \overline{CD}$, what is the value of x?

10x − 54   4x + 42
A   B   C   D

7. In the diagram, what is the value of y?

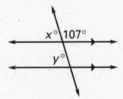

8. Find the value of x that makes $a \parallel b$.

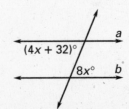

9.

THINK
SOLVE
EXPLAIN

What is the measure in degrees of ∠AXF? Explain your reasoning.

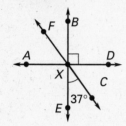

10. Lines a and b are parallel in the diagram. Line c is a transversal. What is the value of x?

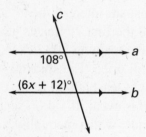

A. 6

B. 10

C. 16

D. 50

11. Which of the following is an equation of a line perpendicular to y − 9 = 2x?

F. $y - 9 = -\frac{1}{2}x$

G. $y + 9 = -2x$

H. $y + 9 = 2x$

I. $y - 9 = \frac{1}{2}x$

12. Which of the following lists 4.8, $\sqrt{23}$, and $4\frac{5}{6}$ in order from **least** to **greatest**?

A. $4.8, \sqrt{23}, 4\frac{5}{6}$

B. $\sqrt{23}, 4.8, 4\frac{5}{6}$

C. $4\frac{5}{6}, \sqrt{23}, 4.8$

D. $\sqrt{23}, 4\frac{5}{6}, 4.8$

13. Given ∠A ≅ ∠D and ∠B ≅ ∠E, find the value of x.

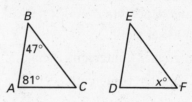

F. 42

G. 52

H. 128

I. 180

14.

THINK
SOLVE
EXPLAIN

Find the slope of $\overleftrightarrow{AC}$ and the slope of $\overleftrightarrow{BD}$. Decide whether $\overleftrightarrow{AC}$ is perpendicular to $\overleftrightarrow{BD}$.

Explain your reasoning.

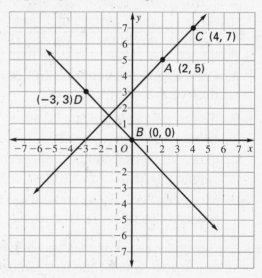

15. The numbers of visitors to a wildlife sanctuary for 7 days were 60, 51, 38, 47, 42, 60, and 66. Which of the following correctly lists the mean, median, and mode of this data?

A. mean: 52; median: 51; mode: 66

B. mean: 57; median: 53.5; mode: 60

C. mean: 52; median: 51; mode: 60

D. mean: 57; median: 53.5; mode: 60

FCAT Diagnostic Test 2

16. Compared to the graph of $y = 4x - 2$, the graph of $y = 4x + 5$

   F. has a greater slope.

   G. has a lesser slope.

   H. has a greater y-intercept.

   I. has a greater x-intercept.

17. Use the table of election results. It shows the numbers of men and women from Districts 1 and 2 who voted for 2 candidates. Based on the information **in the table,** which of the following statements can be verified?

Votes In Districts 1 and 2				
	Men		Women	
Candidate	Chen	Diaz	Chen	Diaz
District 1	94	74	79	95
District 2	63	31	57	79
totals:	157	105	136	174

   A. Chen received about two thirds of the total votes in District 2.

   B. More women voted Diaz because Diaz is a woman.

   C. When all votes from the 2 districts are counted, Diaz has fewer votes.

   D. More District 1 voters chose Chen because Chen lives in District 1.

18. A mako shark can swim at a speed of 30 miles per hour. Choose the best estimate of the number of **yards** a mako shark can swim in one **minute** at that speed.

   F. about 300 yards

   G. about 900 yards

   H. about 1,500 yards

   I. about 2,600 yards

19. | THINK | SOLVE | EXPLAIN | Place an 8-unit by 11-unit rectangle in a coordinate plane and find the length of a diagonal drawn from opposite corners. Explain how you found the length.

20. Rectangle $ABCD$ has diagonal $\overline{BD}$. Which statement correctly describes the congruence of the triangles formed?

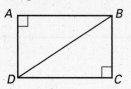

   A. $\triangle ABD \cong \triangle CDB$

   B. $\triangle ABD \cong \triangle BCD$

   C. $\triangle ABD \cong \triangle DCB$

   D. $\triangle ABD \cong \triangle CBD$

21. A school club is organizing a dance to raise money. To spark interest, the students will sell the first 75 tickets at a $2 discount. The remaining 300 tickets will be sold at full price. The students expect to collect at least $2000 from ticket sales for this event. If x represents the full ticket price, which inequality does NOT represent this situation?

   F. $300x + 150 \geq 2000$

   G. $375x - 150 \geq 2000$

   H. $300x + 75(x - 2) \geq 2000$

   I. $300x + 75x - 150 \geq 2000$

22. Solve for x.

$96°$ $4x°$
$(8x - 37)°$
$73°$

   A. 12   **C.** 19

   B. 76   **D.** 115

23. Find the area of the kite.

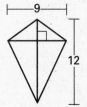

   F. 27 square units

   G. 54 square units

   H. 108 square units

   I. 225 square units

24. Solve for *y*.

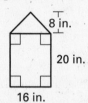

55° x° y°

25. Find the area of the polygon in square inches.

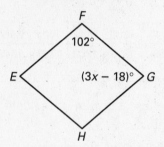

8 in.

20 in.

16 in.

26. The figure *EFGH* is a rhombus. Solve for *x*.

F

102°

E (3x − 18)° G

H

27. What is the value of *x* in the solution of the following system of equations?

$x - y = 8$
$3x - y = 30$

28. Consider the translation that is defined by the coordinate notation $(x, y) \rightarrow (x + 4, y - 3)$. What is the image of $(5, 2)$?

A. $(-1, 9)$

B. $(1, 5)$

C. $(9, -1)$

D. $(9, 5)$

29. How many lines of symmetry does a rhombus have if the rhombus is not a square?

F. none   **H.** two

G. one   **I.** four

30. Find the coordinates of the endpoints of the image of $\overline{AB}$ after a translation of $(x, y) \rightarrow (x - 3, y + 1)$ and a 90° counter-clockwise rotation around the origin.

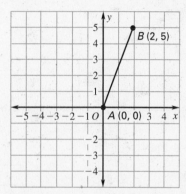

A. $(-1, -3)$ and $(-6, -1)$

B. $(-1, 3)$ and $(-6, -1)$

C. $(-3, -1)$ and $(-6, 1)$

D. $(1, -3)$ and $(6, 1)$

31. A survey reports that when people were asked to choose a favorite drink from Brand A, Brand B, Brand C, and Brand D, 19.7% chose Brand C. If 3000 people were asked, which of the following is a reasonable estimate of the number of people that chose Brand C?

F. about 20   **H.** about 200

G. about 60   **I.** about 600

32. Which conditions are NOT sufficient to prove that $\triangle RST$ is similar to $\triangle PQR$?

A. $m\angle R = m\angle P$ and $m\angle S = m\angle Q$

B. $m\angle S = m\angle Q$ and $\dfrac{RS}{PQ} = \dfrac{ST}{QR}$

C. $\dfrac{RS}{PQ} = \dfrac{ST}{QR}$

D. $\dfrac{RS}{PQ} = \dfrac{ST}{QR} = \dfrac{RT}{PR}$

33. A street sign casts a shadow that is 12 feet long. At the same time, a person who is 5 feet tall casts a shadow that is 7.5 feet long. The triangles below represent this situation.

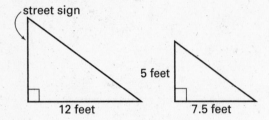

How tall is the street sign?

F. 8 feet

G. 10 feet

H. 14.5 feet

I. 18 feet

34. A company gave all of its employees a 3.5% pay increase one year. One employee earned an annual salary of $40,000 before the pay increase. What was the employee's annual salary after the pay increase?

A. $40,003.50

B. $41,400

C. $52,500

D. $140,000

35. You choose a marble at random from a jar holding 5 red, 1 green, and 3 yellow marbles. You also choose a coin at random from a bag holding 2 quarters and 2 dimes. What is the probability that you choose a red marble and a dime?

F. $\frac{5}{18}$

G. $\frac{7}{13}$

H. $\frac{6}{11}$

I. $\frac{5}{9}$

36. Find the area of the figure.

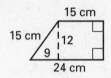

A. 276 square centimeters

B. 234 square centimeters

C. 180 square centimeters

D. 54 square centimeters

37.
| THINK |
| SOLVE |
| EXPLAIN |

The table shows the number of video tapes rented from a video rental store for 6 months.

Month	March	April	May	June	July
Tape rentals	1952	1895	1802	1731	1649

Part A Make a scatter plot of the data in the table.

Part B On the scatter plot, as time passes, what happens to the number of video tapes rented?

Part C Predict the number of tapes rented in August. Express your prediction as a range of values. Explain how you made your prediction.

38. Find the length of $\overarc{AB}$ in feet. Round to the nearest tenth of a foot. Use 3.14 for π.

39. The figure is a circle in a square. Find the area of the shaded region in square inches. Use 3.14 for π. Round your answer to thte nearest tenth.

9 in.

9 in.

40. 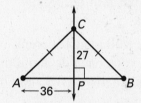 In the diagram, $\overleftrightarrow{CP} \perp \overline{AB}$ and $\overline{AC} \cong \overline{BC}$. Find the perimeter of $\triangle ABC$.

C

27

A ←36→ P B

41. Carolyn is painting all the surfaces on the inside and the outside of a box except for the lid. The box is in the shape of a rectangular prism that is 7 inches long, 5 inches wide, and 2 inches high. How many square inches will she be covering with paint?

42. A sphere has a radius of 7 feet. What is the area of a planar cross section that passes through the center of the sphere?

F. 7π square feet

G. $7\pi^2$ square feet

H. 14π square feet

I. 49π square feet

43. The table shows some values of a function.

Input x	−2	−1	0	1	2
Output y	6	3	0	−3	?

What is the value of y when $x = 2$?

A. −6 **C.** 3

B. −2 **D.** 6

44. THINK SOLVE EXPLAIN Name the solid that could be made using the net below. Then find the surface area and the volume of the solid.

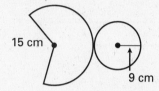

15 cm

9 cm

45. In the circle shown, what is the value of x?

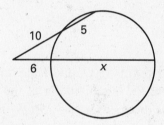

10 5

6 x

F. 9

G. 13

H. 15

I. 19

46. Which of the following is an equation of a circle with center $(2, -4)$ and a radius of 3?

A. $(x - 2)^2 + (y - 4)^2 = 9$

B. $(x + 2)^2 + (y - 4)^2 = 9$

C. $(x - 2)^2 + (y + 4)^2 = 9$

D. $(x - 2)^2 - (y - 4)^2 = 9$

47. Let $\vec{w} = \langle 2, -9 \rangle$ and $\vec{z} = \langle -1, 12 \rangle$. Find $\vec{w} + \vec{z}$.

F. $\langle -1, -3 \rangle$

G. $\langle 1, 3 \rangle$

H. $\langle -3, 1 \rangle$

I. $\langle 3, 1 \rangle$

48. In the triangle below, cos X is equal to which of the following?

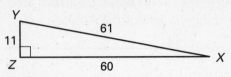

A. $\frac{11}{61}$

B. $\frac{11}{60}$

C. $\frac{60}{61}$

D. $\frac{61}{60}$

49. The points P, Q, and R lie on a circle. Segment PR is a diameter of the circle. What is the measure of ∠PQR in degrees?

50. Find the area of the triangle to the nearest square unit.

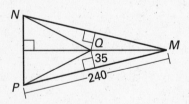

51. The perpendicular bisectors of the sides of △MNP meet at point Q. Find QN.

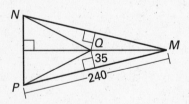

52. THINK SOLVE EXPLAIN   Use the diagram below.

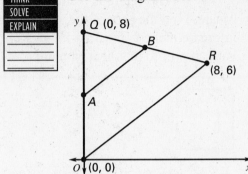

Part A Find the midpoint A of $\overline{OQ}$ and the midpoint B of $\overline{QR}$. Show your work.

Part B Using the Midpoint Theorem, what can you conclude about the relationship between $\overline{AB}$ and $\overline{OR}$?

Part C Use your results from Part A to verify your conclusions in Part B.

Name _____ Date _____

FCAT Diagnostic Test 1
Answer Sheet

Use the Answer Sheets to record your answers to the FCAT Diagnostic Test 1.

1 Ⓐ Ⓑ Ⓒ Ⓓ   **2** Ⓕ Ⓖ Ⓗ Ⓘ   **3** Ⓐ Ⓑ Ⓒ Ⓓ   **4** Ⓕ Ⓖ Ⓗ Ⓘ

5 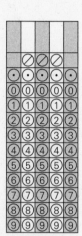   **6**    **7**    **8**

---

9 THINK SOLVE EXPLAIN   What is the measure, in degrees, of ∠AXF in your test booklet?

Angle measure _____

Reasoning:

---

10 Ⓐ Ⓑ Ⓒ Ⓓ   **11** Ⓕ Ⓖ Ⓗ Ⓘ   **12** Ⓐ Ⓑ Ⓒ Ⓓ   **13** Ⓕ Ⓖ Ⓗ Ⓘ

Name _____ Date _____

FCAT Diagnostic Test 1
Answer Sheet

14 THINK SOLVE EXPLAIN Find the slope of $\overleftrightarrow{AC}$ and the slope of $\overleftrightarrow{BD}$ pictured in your test booklet.

Slope of $\overleftrightarrow{AC}$: _____

Slope of $\overleftrightarrow{BD}$: _____

Is $\overleftrightarrow{AC}$ perpendicular to $\overleftrightarrow{BD}$? Explain.

---

15 Ⓐ Ⓑ Ⓒ Ⓓ **16** Ⓕ Ⓖ Ⓗ Ⓘ **17** Ⓐ Ⓑ Ⓒ Ⓓ **18** Ⓕ Ⓖ Ⓗ Ⓘ

---

19 THINK SOLVE EXPLAIN Place a 5-unit by 7-unit rectangle in a coordinate plane and draw a diagonal.

Graph

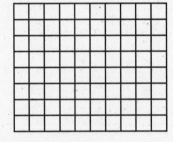

How long is the diagonal? Explain.

164 **Geometry**
Sunshine State Standards Support Book

Copyright © McDougal Littell,
a division of Houghton Mifflin Company

FCAT Diagnostic Test 1
Answer Sheet

20 (A) (B) (C) (D) **21** (F) (G) (H) (I) **22** (A) (B) (C) (D) **23** (F) (G) (H) (I)

24  **25**  **26**  **27**

28 (A) (B) (C) (D) **29** (F) (G) (H) (I) **30** (A) (B) (C) (D) **31** (F) (G) (H) (I)

32 (A) (B) (C) (D) **33** (F) (G) (H) (I) **34** (A) (B) (C) (D) **35** (F) (G) (H) (I)

36 (A) (B) (C) (D)

37 *Part A* Make a scatter plot of the data in the table in your test booklet.

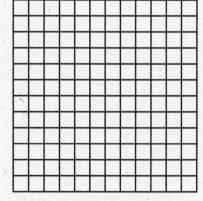

Part B As time passes, what happens to the number of movie screens?

Part C Predict the number of movie screens in 2005. Explain how you made your prediction.

FCAT Diagnostic Test 1
Answer Sheet

38 　39 　40 　41

42   　43

44 Name the solid that could be made using the net. Then find the surface area and the volume of the solid. Use 3.14 for π.

solid: _____

surface area of solid:

volume of solid:

FCAT Diagnostic Test 1
Answer Sheet

45 Ⓕ Ⓖ Ⓗ Ⓘ **46** Ⓐ Ⓑ Ⓒ Ⓓ **47** Ⓕ Ⓖ Ⓗ Ⓘ **48** Ⓐ Ⓑ Ⓒ Ⓓ

49  **50**  **51**

52   ***Part A*** Find the midpoint of $\overline{OQ}$ and the midpoint of $\overline{QR}$ for $\triangle OQR$ in your test booklet. Show your work.

Midpoint of $\overline{OQ}$: _____   Midpoint of $\overline{QR}$: _____

Part B Using the Midpoint Theorem, what can you conclude about the relationship between $\overline{AB}$ and $\overline{OR}$?

Part C Use your results from Part A to verify your conclusions in Part B.

Name _____ Date _____

FCAT Diagnostic Test 2
Answer Sheet

Use the Answer Sheets to record your answers to the FCAT Diagnostic Test 2.

1 Ⓐ Ⓑ Ⓒ Ⓓ   **2** Ⓕ Ⓖ Ⓗ Ⓘ   **3** Ⓐ Ⓑ Ⓒ Ⓓ   **4** Ⓕ Ⓖ Ⓗ Ⓘ

5    **6**    **7**    **8**

---

9 | THINK / SOLVE / EXPLAIN | What is the measure, in degrees, of $\angle AXF$ in your test booklet?

Angle measure _____

Reasoning:

---

10 Ⓐ Ⓑ Ⓒ Ⓓ   **11** Ⓕ Ⓖ Ⓗ Ⓘ   **12** Ⓐ Ⓑ Ⓒ Ⓓ   **13** Ⓕ Ⓖ Ⓗ Ⓘ

FCAT Diagnostic Test 2
Answer Sheet

  Find the slope of $\overleftrightarrow{AC}$ and the slope of $\overleftrightarrow{BD}$ pictured in your booklet.

Slope of $\overleftrightarrow{AC}$: _____

Slope of $\overleftrightarrow{BD}$: _____

Is $\overleftrightarrow{AC}$ perpendicular to $\overleftrightarrow{BD}$? Explain.

  Ⓐ Ⓑ Ⓒ Ⓓ   Ⓕ Ⓖ Ⓗ Ⓘ   Ⓐ Ⓑ Ⓒ Ⓓ   Ⓕ Ⓖ Ⓗ Ⓘ

⑲ Place a 8-unit by 11-unit rectangle in a coordinate plane and draw a diagonal.

Graph

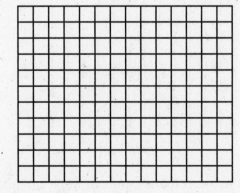

How long is the diagonal? Explain.

GRADE 10 Continued

FCAT Diagnostic Test 2
Answer Sheet

20 Ⓐ Ⓑ Ⓒ Ⓓ **21** Ⓕ Ⓖ Ⓗ Ⓘ **22** Ⓐ Ⓑ Ⓒ Ⓓ **23** Ⓕ Ⓖ Ⓗ Ⓘ

24 | **25** | **26** | **27**

28 Ⓐ Ⓑ Ⓒ Ⓓ **29** Ⓕ Ⓖ Ⓗ Ⓘ **30** Ⓐ Ⓑ Ⓒ Ⓓ **31** Ⓕ Ⓖ Ⓗ Ⓘ

32 Ⓐ Ⓑ Ⓒ Ⓓ **33** Ⓕ Ⓖ Ⓗ Ⓘ **34** Ⓐ Ⓑ Ⓒ Ⓓ **35** Ⓕ Ⓖ Ⓗ Ⓘ

36 Ⓐ Ⓑ Ⓒ Ⓓ

37 THINK SOLVE EXPLAIN

Part A Make a scatter plot of the data in the table in your test booklet.

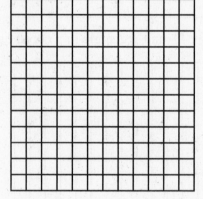

Part B As time passes, what happens to the number of tapes rented?

Part C Predict the number of tapes rented in August. Explain how you made your prediction.

Name _____ Date _____

FCAT Diagnostic Test 2
Answer Sheet

42 (F) (G) (H) (I)   **43** (A) (B) (C) (D)

44

THINK
SOLVE
EXPLAIN

Name the solid that could be made using the net. Then find the surface area and the volume of the solid. Use 3.14 for π.

solid: _____

surface area of solid:

volume of solid:

Name _____ Date _____

FCAT Diagnostic Test 2
Answer Sheet

45 Ⓕ Ⓖ Ⓗ Ⓘ **46** Ⓐ Ⓑ Ⓒ Ⓓ **47** Ⓕ Ⓖ Ⓗ Ⓘ **48** Ⓐ Ⓑ Ⓒ Ⓓ

49  **50**  **51**

52

THINK
SOLVE
EXPLAIN

Part A Find the midpoint of $\overline{OQ}$ and the midpoint of $\overline{QR}$ for $\triangle OQR$ in your test booklet. Show your work.

Midpoint of $\overline{OQ}$: _____   *Midpoint of $\overline{QR}$:* _____

Part B Using the Midpoint Theorem, what can you conclude about the relationship between AB and OR?

Part C Use your results from Part A to verify your conclusions in Part B.

172 Geometry
Sunshine State Standards Support Book